LIQUOR

*The Servant
of Man*

LIQUOR

The Servant of Man

by MORRIS E. CHAFETZ

Little, Brown and Company · Boston · Toronto

Published simultaneously in Canada
by Little, Brown & Company (Canada) Limited

PRINTED IN THE UNITED STATES OF AMERICA

1926

To my hopes for the future:
Gary, Marc, Adam

Author's Note

A book on liquor needs no introduction. All of us from early moments of awareness have ideas about alcohol, its use and nonuse. Those who wish to retain their ill-begotten fears and fantasies about nature's gift need read no further.

All authors recount their indebtedness to others in the preparation of their work. My story is no different, perhaps only more so. If the book is a success, those who have helped will consider that acknowledgment sufficient. If the book is ill received, they will bless my name for their anonymity. Some of the greatest joys of life have been eliminated by overconcern with scientific accuracy. Accuracy is admirable in the laboratory or in writing scientific treatises. I'm happy to say this is not a scientific treatise, just a pleasant look at liquor.

M.E.C.

Intervale, New Hampshire

About the Author

FOR THE past twenty years Morris Chafetz has pursued a vigorous and successful career in medicine. During much of that time, he has held appointments at the Massachusetts General Hospital in Boston, advancing from Fellow in Psychiatry to his present position of Assistant Clinical Professor in Psychiatry on the Faculty of Medicine at Harvard University. Through his training and a capacity for hard work, he has accomplished a solid foundation in the varied disciplines of psychiatry, including research investigations with backward schizophrenic patients and victims of Parkinson's disease.

When, in 1954, Dr. Chafetz was offered a position in the hospital's Alcohol Clinic, the nature of his work changed abruptly; it has since taken him over most of the United States and much of the world — observing, studying, and lecturing on the use of alcohol and its problems. In the beginning, Dr. Chafetz knew little about alcoholism except that it was a field with low prestige; since that time he has undertaken extensive research and made major contributions to the field, including authorship of more than thirty clinical and research papers. Thanks to his indefatigable interest in the subject, he has done much to help reduce the terrible onus that has traditionally burdened people with alcohol-related problems.

Along with his study of alcoholism, Dr. Chafetz has taken on an unusual challenge in exploring both sides of the coin. His joie de vivre, his enthusiasm, energy, and facility of communicating and relating to all kinds of people have made him aware that too many of us have lost the ability to enjoy the simplest pleasures in a busy life; by focusing on the negative aspects, we have forgotten the positive pleasures of this marvelous social tool, alcohol. Fools and unjust men, he feels, have brought scandal on an excellent creature; in *Liquor: The Servant of Man,* he seeks to prove his point: that man can — and should — drink with pleasure and without fear.

THE EDITORS

Contents

LIQUOR

*The Servant
of Man*

Introduction

EXISTENCE alone is not enough for man. Within whatever period he walks the earth, he hopes to experience
more than eating, eliminating, sleeping and procreat-
ing. The range of his experience, and thereby his possible delight, will depend somewhat upon the chances
he is willing to take. If he ventures far, his risks are
great — but so are the returns. If he plays it safe, tight
to the vest, his risks are much less — but so too are the
pleasures of living.

I am not so presumptuous as to tell others how to
live, for there is for me no greater insult than the imposition of my values onto my fellows. But I have been
bothered recently by what I view as the mood of the
times. True, our Puritan ethic of controlled emotion,
the avoidance of spontaneity and uninhibited pleasure,
has always made us a bit afraid to let go. Lately, however, there stalks the specter of a safety consciousness
that stifles living. We are beseeched not to smoke because we might develop lung cancer; we are warned
about driving carefully because forty-three thousand
people die each year on the roads; our women nervously
feel themselves for the lumps that signal dreaded

cancer of the breast; and we constantly scrutinize our children and invade their privacy to make sure they are not deviating from some healthy, mysterious norm. Butter and other delicious fats are better avoided because the cholesterol level might go up. Soon, I expect, someone will suggest that we avoid bathrooms because most home accidents happen there!

And, of course, there is alcohol, a subject close to my heart and stomach.

The admonitions against alcohol are unbelievable, and date from antiquity. If you drink, some say, you'll become an alcoholic, or a drunkard. At the very least, your life will be shortened, or you will become illegitimately pregnant, or commit a crime, damage your brain, become an addict, smash your car, or otherwise go to pot! The evils that spirits, beer and wine portend are horrendous (even though the temperance workers — having won the war only to lose the peace — have essentially fled the field). Hide the bottle from your kids, make special laws for its use, don't let it go through the mails, and for heaven's sake don't advertise it. Mind you, all this we deliberate, determine and decide even as we imbibe alcohol in great quantities.

My concern with all this emphasis on safety today is that it is taking the fun out of life. Certainly if you fly or ski or smoke or drink or enjoy sex some harm may come to you. You can be killed in a plane crash or you can break a leg skiing. You can develop cancer, bronchitis or a hacking cough from smoking, or you can drink yourself silly, stupid and sick. And I don't have to spell out how sex can get you into all sorts of trouble, real or imagined!

The fact is, such things don't have to happen — and to the vast majority they don't. Most people who fly do not die in crashes, most who ski do not suffer injury, most who smoke do not develop cancer, most who drink do not become drunk or alcoholic, and most who enjoy sex do not get into trouble. And yet the scare-mongers, the pleasure-killers, the safety-seekers shout with loud clarion calls their messages of doom. The emphasis is all negative; the don't's drown the do's. It is as though a minority of scared, unhappy people have successfully attempted to kill the pleasure for us all.

In our inability to let go and live, we have even turned leisure into labor. Just as we have become safety conscious, so have we become "do it just right" conscious. No one in his right mind would think of swinging a golf club and smacking a ball just for fun. Oh, no! First you must acquire an exclusive club membership, buy the proper clothes and clubs, take some expensive lessons, then make an appointment far in advance to tee off. The fact that you might be more inclined to play and relax at another hour on another day is not important. You must predict far in advance how you intend to feel — and then you'd better feel that way.

And, of course, fishing has gone by the board. Recently one of my sons was foolish enough to want to try fishing and I was willing to spend a dollar or two to get him started. I thought a pole of bamboo, a length of twine, a box of ten-cent hooks and a can of freshly dug worms ought to do the trick. The sporting-goods salesman goggled at us as though we were from another planet. Fishing is for specialists! He asked my boy and me so many detailed questions, obvious no doubt to the educated, about spinners, flies, lines and so forth, that we were both humiliated. I never realized that the relaxation I enjoyed as a child, of flipping a line into a creek and lying upon my back to watch the panorama of the world float by in the sky, was now a leisure of labor, not love.

Skiing and sailing, painting and potting, music listening and book buying have become highly intricate, expensive and laborious. We must do things right and not merely for relaxation or pleasure. As someone recently noted, society with its genius for self-adjustment will yield a day when after a hard weekend of leisure, a man will go thankfully off to his job to relax.

Now, for more years than I care to remember, I've toiled in the field of alcoholism. It's not a pleasant field, nor an easy one. My patients are ashamed of what has befallen them, as are their families and friends. Society responds as though they suffered from the plague. Indeed, the destruction from alcoholism is great, the tragedy unbelievable, and this I know firsthand from my work.

To sum up: alcoholism is a major public health problem; *liquor is not.*

Therefore, this book is written to the average drinker, not to the problem drinker. Of course, many people who are diagnosed as "problem drinkers" are not really that at all. The reformer, whose temperament is similar, finds his narcotic in crusading; he is not in my audience either. The problem drinker and the reformer are the extremes — they can be cured, but they often relocate and turn to something stronger.

No, this book addresses the larger crowd: the man who drinks liquor because he likes it and the man who thinks he ought not; the man who cures colds with it and the man who swears off for fear of cirrhosis; the man who coats his stomach by drinking olive oil beforehand and the man who drinks milk afterward; the man who takes soda and the man who does not; the man who has to get up twice in the night and the man who groans all day Sunday. If you are there, you are in the great majority. You know a lot more about liquor than did the same majority five thousand years ago, but you are not swearing off any faster.

Perhaps you don't believe what you read. Today the book stands are drenched with liquor literature full of terms like "hidden alcoholic," "problem drinker" and "alcoholism." Try reading one of these books without recognizing yourself in there among the terms. This book may be more "liquor literature," true, but it will be different, because this author does not believe that most of you belong among the problem drinkers. He does not think that other writers on the story of liquor place correct emphasis on this fact: ninety-five per cent of the people who drink have no alcohol problem. This is a story thousands of years old, and we are still telling it. I am not saying the other writings are untrue, but that their focus — on problems, extremes, physiology, pharmacology, dire predictions — is self-limited.

But the whys and wherefores are superficial. Precious little has been presented to explain the failure of countless prohibitions. There has been nothing about why we go on drinking, or why alcohol should have continued to exist at all. In recent years a few answers have been unearthed by different men in different places; some are clearly proven facts, some are conjectures, some individual opinions. These are gathered and submitted here. They show that liquor came before civilization — and they shape this author's opinion that civilization might not have evolved without it. Liquor drinking is a part of human behavior in which mankind has indulged forever, although he suspects it is wrong (but hasn't investigated very far, for fear of learning for sure). This writer has investigated it thoroughly, and he believes that it is not wrong.

Among the many things said about drink you will find such statements as: "My grandfather drank like a fish all his life and lived to be ninety-six." Or this one: "My grandfather drank himself to death at forty-eight." Or: "Make mine a double; I'm tired." Or: "Make mine a double; I'm cold." Or: "Make it light; I'm getting fat." Or more often: "I wouldn't have done it if I hadn't been tight."

True or false? The answers sound simple enough, but right or wrong answers are not so easily come by. Surely there is no other human custom — save sex — which is buried in such a mass of myths and misconceptions. But we alert the reader that this book intends to weigh the answers, for a change, on the *positive* side of liquor.

Nor is there any plan to extol moderation. What exactly is "moderation"? Curiously, moderate drinking is beyond definition; yet everybody knows what it is. We know of a man who has not gone to bed without heavy drinking one night in forty years — but he is a moderate drinker. He can surely afford to drink, he runs his corporation effectively and intelligently, he does not get out of self-control, he never prowls, he plays at games that call for lots of exercise, he smokes heavily, and he feels and looks well. And I like what Churchill is reputed to have said: "I have taken more out of alcohol than alcohol has taken out of me."

Immoderate drinking, on the other hand, means problem drinking, or alcoholism. Some say that only a hairline separates the social or moderate drinker from the alcoholic. Don't you believe it — a grand canyon separates them. The difference between them is usually described in the way that the social drinker uses liquor to heighten his momentary enjoyment, while the alcoholic uses it to escape reality. Still wrong. Drinking does not take the edge off reality just for the alcoholic; it does so for everyone, or no one would do it. The crucial difference lies in their two definitions of reality; to one, reality is a dull grind that can use a bit of brightening; to the other, it means a state of self-destructive illness which we psychiatrists are still busily describing. More than a hairline exists between the two. One thing is certain: the social drinker is in the vast majority. If that were not true, there would hardly be a human race.

What is liquor all about? Why does a drink have the effect it does? What happens inside you when you take one, or ten? What is the effect of a hundred thousand drinks over a lifetime, or on an entire race? Are there any people who have never known about liquor? And if so, where are they? Why is one man a "two-fisted drinker" while another is a "two-drink man"? How about "swearing off"? Why does food "kill the kick"? Does liquor make you fat? What are the business advantages of drinking, if any? What about teenage drinking, alcohol and crime, drinking and driving? What are the physical or psychological benefits of drinking, if any? What effect does alcohol have on the sex life? How long has drinking been going on? Who started it?

Let's take a look at some of these questions and try to answer them.

1

Background

C_2H_5OH. That is the chemist's symbol for ethyl alcohol, a poison taken internally by human beings for thirty thousand years — and the practice shows no sign of stopping. Exactly how it all began is something else. Just as we know not who turned fire to man's service, who started marriage, or who invented the wheel, so we know not what primeval low-forehead forgot a pot of fruit and then took a swig of the fermented result.

One tale discusses liquor and the creation of the world. Even then, the forces of good were contesting the forces of evil for possession of the earth. The good, as usual, were victorious, but in the course of their victory some good gods died, and wherever they fell the soil sprouted vine. This battle raged over the far reaches of the earth, spreading wide the distribution of the vine. The fruit of these "divine" vines yielded the blood of grape (blood of god), which imparted to the imbiber the spirit of the god. Thus the closeness of the exudate of grape and spiritual experience flits across the eons of time from antiquity to the present.

The Persians relate the accidental discovery of drink to love. A prince loved the grape to the point of autumn depression. To prevent his sadness, he stored his luscious grapes for future use. But alas when in time he tried to eat them, he was disappointed to find a strange substance indeed. He labeled the stuff "poison," which made it instantly attractive to one of his wives who had lost favor and was trying to do herself in. After one cup, the desire diminished. After another, she could not even recall her sadness! And after a few more, she had the nerve to tell her husband of the discovery of the "delightful poison."

As an unknown sage said in 1690: "You say man learned first to build a fire and then to ferment his liquor. Had he but reversed the process we should have no need of flint and tinder to this day." However and by whom alcohol came into existence, much has happened because of it. Some contend it started the first stable community life. Early man was nomadic. Several years are required to develop a producing vineyard, however, and the anthropologists say that pursuit of the vine marks the change from a scattered human race to a settled one. It may well be that man was brewer before baker; lover of liquor before lover of home.

Not only is the discoverer of liquor unknown to us, but even the refined and finished art of vine culture dates too far back for historical record. Mythology, as noted, has no such problem. Only the tenth generation after Adam, Noah is named by the Old Testament as the first to plant a vineyard (this, mind you, after his six hundredth birthday!). The flood had subsided and Noah, making his covenant with God, agreed to behave. The Bible records that he "began to be a husbandman, and he planted a vineyard." He made wine from his grapes and he "was drunken."

Mohammedan tradition ascribes the first planting to his son Ham and says Satan was there, watering the ground with peacocks' blood, sprinkling the leaves with apes' blood, drenching the green grapes with lions' blood and, when the grapes were ripe, with the blood of swine. The explanation: "The first glass makes a man animated, his vivacity great, his colors heightened. In this condition he is like the peacock. When the fumes of the liquor rise into his head, he is gay, leaps and gambols as an ape. Drunkenness takes possession of him, he is like a furious lion. When it is at its height he is like the swine; he falls and grovels on the ground, stretches himself out and goes to sleep." That was written a long time ago, but the picture is strangely familiar.

One of the reasons suggested for Mohammed's law against drink was that the prophet desired to make Moslem rites and habits as different as possible from those that were practiced by the followers of other religions, in particular to widen the gap between Christians and Moslems. Wine, he pointed out, is the high symbol in the most holy of Christian ceremonies. Furthermore, alcohol creates thirst and thirst is to be avoided where water is scarce.

"Wine," sings a poet, "digesteth food and disperseth care and dispelleth flatulence and clarifieth the blood and cleareth the complexion and quickeneth the body and hearteneth the hen-hearted and fortifieth the sexual power in many, but to name all its virtue would be tedious. In short, had not Allah forbidden it, there were naught on the face of the earth to stand in its stead."

After the first vineyard, it did not take long for the popularity of liquor drinking to gain speed. The Old Testament does not lack for references to it. Lot drank himself sodden and Nabal did not precisely despise it. While wandering through the desert, Moses sent spies ahead to explore the land, and it is reported that what appealed to them most was the size of the grape clusters they found.

In any event, it is thought that beverage alcohol has been in use for some three hundred centuries — so at least we know it cannot all be blamed on dry martinis! True historical references do not appear until the Hebrew script, on Babylonian tablets, and in ancient Egyptian carvings picturing the manufacture of wine. This is a mere sixty or seventy centuries ago, but it nevertheless represents a part of earliest recorded history. Wine was made in China before 2000 B.C., and archeologists recently unearthed the ruins of a huge winery twenty-six hundred years old at the ancient city of Gibeon, near Jerusalem. This winery had a storage capacity of thirty thousand gallons of wine. Found also were stone presses in which grapes had been crushed. The wine industry at Gibeon is mentioned frequently in the Bible; wine making ended when the city was destroyed about 600 B.C.

The Phoenicians took the "vine that bears the wine" into ancient Greece in 600 B.C. Plato and Socrates and Aristotle and Aeschylus loved and were inspired by it, and Sappho wrote songs about it. Wine and their god Dionysus went with the Greeks to civilize the Etruscans. The Romans established vine growing as an important agricultural pursuit, and after Caesar's conquest of Gaul it spread to western Europe. Every country along the Mediterranean has made wine.

Between A.D. 500 and 1400, Europe was the vine-growing center of the world. During this period, medieval Christians interested themselves in vine growing as in other arts, and monasteries developed many refinements of viticulture. The monks fostered the winemakers' art in all parts of Europe; wine inspired poets like Dante and Chaucer and Shakespeare, and they sang eloquently of it. Incidently, references to alcohol are not confined to grape-growing countries. The oldest Scandinavian sagas refer to malt liquors. Egyptian excavations more than six thousand years old depict their drinking customs — for example, a man being carried home from a bender on the heads of his slaves. It seems a shame that this poor Egyptian gentleman cannot know that now, after six thousand additional years of practice, people are still losing bouts like that one.

The first appearance of liquor in Egypt, and also in Greece, was attributed to a god: to Osiris in Egypt and Dionysus in Greece. Judging by ancient writings, temperance workers sprang up as early as liquor, and so the best opportunities for unrestrained drinking were provided by religious rites and festivals. Since drinking was an accepted part of these festivities, critical voices were muted. Nevertheless, Isaiah was scathing in his attack on those who consumed strong drink, while Nazirites and Rechabites were among the earliest teetotalers.

Some of these ancient drinking parties, incidentally, were of no niggardly proportions. To many ancients, a present-day hard weekend of drinking would have been merely a cocktail hour. They carried on for days and longer. One event was reported to have lasted day and night without interruption for a full year. And the quality of the liquor they drank is even more remarkable than their endurance. It is said that distillation was known at least one hundred years before Christ, but it was not much in use. They drank wine. (The question whether you can get drunk on wine was settled some time ago, and it is a sure thing that anyone who has ever done so remembers it, very acutely, the next day.) But although too much even of a good wine treats you badly, the wine the ancients used was kept in receptacles made of hides which were treated with oil, and to the liquor itself resin and salt were added. When you consider that it was not unusual for a drinker to down three gallons of this nauseous mixture at a sitting, it is easy to understand why there was no need, or incentive, to invent stomach pumps!

The ancients really wanted liquor. Men even drank hemlock so that the fear of death by poison would scare them into deeper potations of wine as an antidote. They were taken out of hot baths half dead and stumbled back to their nightcaps. The Roman debauches are old stuff because they had many articulate writers to tell about them, but the same revels occurred in other countries too, and in other ages. For instance, there was a notable entertainment given for Queen Elizabeth I, with twenty thousand guests attending, each averaging a gallon of ale. By the end of this memorable evening, three hundred sixty-five hogsheads of beer had been consumed.

As in the present, some of the historic bacchanalia could not have been funny to the participants. In China during the year 2150 B.C. occurred the unfortunate alcoholic experience of two important men named He and Ho. They were royal astronomers charged with keeping the people informed about what transpired in the heavens. But alas, He and Ho got drunk and let an eclipse creep up on them unawares. The prince who received the imperial edict to mete out their punishment addressed them thus: "Now here are He and Ho. They have entirely subverted their virtue and are sunk and lost in wine. They have allowed the regulations of Heaven to get into disorder. From the first day of

the last month, the Sun and Moon did meet harmoni-
ously. The blind musicians beat their drums; the inferior
officers and common people bustled and ran about.
He and Ho, however, as if they were mere personators
of the dead, heard nothing and knew nothing, so
stupidly went they astray from their duty in the matter
of Heavenly appearances. They have rendered themselves liable to death. The statutes say, when astronomers predict ahead of the proper time, let them be
put to death without mercy; also when they are behind
the time, let them be put to death."

He and Ho were not unique in turning to the bottle
as a relief from this sort of responsibility.

It is true that some Chinese monarchs tried to force
the abolition of alcohol with banishments and execu-
tions. One man who invented an intoxicating drink
made from rice was banished in 2285 B.C. A temperance
killjoy tells the episode with pleasure, exclaiming that
Chinese rulers from earliest times have taken a "remarkably advanced position" against liquor and that
as a result the Chinese have a high standard as to this
vice. Unfortunately, the writer fails to discuss another
narcotic, called opium, for which the standard was not
so high and which ruled many millions of Chinese.

The same writer also regretted to discover some
"bad" monarchs, all alcohol-maddened tyrants and
voluptuaries. Kia, who ruled about 1770 B.C., particularly
incensed him. Kia had concubines. What generosi-
ties he accorded his ordinary concubines is unknown,
but to his favorite, at least, he gave "a splendid palace,

and in the parks which surrounded it, a lake of wine at which three thousand men drank at the sound of a drum while the trees hung with dead meat and hills of flesh were piled up."

By contrast, Diamond Jim Brady was a tattered urchin passing out Alcoholics Anonymous pamphlets. Doubtless many readers would not mind having looked in on such a scene, and, judging from the luscious literary description, one cannot help but wonder if the killjoy temperance writer would not like to have joined in too.

There is indeed little relationship between a biased writer and the specialized scientific writer. Biased writers might contribute more if they did not consistently mistake matters on which scholars have been agreed for years — for instance, in ascribing to drink the declines and falls of empires, races and people. Rome, of course, is a classic example. The biased writer states: "The light of Rome went out in bacchanalian revels." Now, there is no one scientifically accepted approach to studying declines and falls. Even within any single method there is still controversy over the complex cause of the fall of the Roman Empire, and about the only thing known for certain is that the phenomenon was *not* due simply to overdrinking.

The British since the time of the Druids have used drink continuously and conspicuously, and only in recent years have they possibly declined but certainly not fallen. Through the ages, however, heavy drinking was so prevalent that there was always fear of invasion.

As early as A.D. 81, in a move to check intemperance, the Roman emperor Domitian ordered the destruction of half the British vineyards and commanded that no more be planted without imperial right. Much later, James I passed drastic laws for the punishment of drunkenness; these were ineffectual and during the reign of his successor Charles I hard drinking was such a problem that regulations were introduced to suppress liquor altogether — and these too failed. During the Commonwealth, drunkenness was still so prevalent in England that other nations called her "The Land of the Drunkards." In fact, at no period have the residents of the British Isles lost their relish for liquor. Nevertheless, they might be said to have done at least as well for themselves as others such as the Mohammedans and the Buddhists, who are not supposed to drink at all.

Investigations of the ancient Indians, Persians, Arabians, the Israelites, the Thracians and Scythians, Parthians, Illyrians, Tapyrians, Lydians, Cambrians — and plenty of others this writer never heard of before — disclose alcoholic habits at least on a par with our own today. References to all ancient peoples can be given telling of their gross misuse of alcohol. But the statement cannot be intelligently refuted that none of them declined or fell because of it.

Individuals, on the other hand, have indeed declined and fallen because of liquor, as they are doing now, and certainly battles have been lost because of it. Liquor has been used strategically in war and in diplomacy (and still is), not just by a few dirty tricksters, but by all. Salome, for instance, has always been well advertised as a whore who led Herod into intemperate habits and so charmed him with her splendid dancing that she was able to get a man's head cut off. It was a seamy plot which has not won her many admirers. But consider too the reputation of Judith, who had loftier reasons. The Assyrians, under an ill-starred captain named Holofernes, were about to enter Judea. A book of the Apocrypha acquaints us with Judith: "A woman of wonderful courage and surpassing beauty, who effected the deliverance. In company with her maid she visited the tent of Holofernes, and cunningly held out to him the hopes of effecting the speedy and easy capture of the inhabitants. Holofernes, fascinated by the charms of her person, prepared for his fair guest a feast, at which he drank much more wine than he had drunk at any time in one day since he was born. In the hour of night Judith approached the couch of the chief who was filled with wine, and cut off his head. Her people were greatly encouraged by this event and suddenly fell upon the Assyrians, who were in utter amazement and fright, and slew them with a terrible slaughter. . . ." Possibly there is something good to be said on both sides: Salome at least did not do the cutting herself; on the other hand, Judith was not the kind of woman who would visit a man's tent unchaperoned.

Using liquor in wars and battles was such everyday strategy that ancient writers wondered why their respective protagonists did not obtain the wisdom to forbid drinking in the field. The literature of Herodotus, Athenaeus and Horace recounts plenty of hair-raisers on this subject, and some of the descriptions of the butcheries are beautiful, at least in their completeness. One episode concerns Germanicus, whose spies reported that the warlike tribe he wished to attack was planning to have a festival. That meant enough to Germanicus so that he waited for the feast night, and then his army sneaked up on them:

The barbarians were sunk in sleep and wine, some stretched on their beds, others at full length under the tables; without a guard, without a post, and without a sentinel on duty. No appearance of war was seen, only the effect of savage riot; the languor of debauch. The whole of them were slaughtered, without the attackers suffering the loss of a single life.

Cyaxares, king of Media and Persia, went a step further. On the pretext of friendship he invited the Scythians to a drinking feast, and Herodotus takes two sentences to finish the story: "The greater part of them became intoxicated, and in that state were destroyed. Cyaxares thus obtained possession of Asia."

This was pretty low hospitality, true, but even the Lord was constrained to employ similar action. The Bible reports that when Belshazzar and his reveling Babylonians were living in sin, the Lord said, "In their heat I will make their feast, and I will make them drunken, that they may rejoice, and sleep a perpetual sleep, and not wake. . . ." This divine assistance tipped the advantage to Cyrus, who was the chosen instru-

ment of the Almighty for punishing the Babylonians —
and everyone knows what Cyrus did to the Babylonians. One recorder says, "the Babylonians fell an easy
prey to her intrepid conquerors." He goes on to say
that the predictions of the prophets "were never more
awfully or signally fulfilled. The prophets," he says,
"frequently exclaim in the most energetic language
against the intemperance which prevailed, and present
in glowing language the awful consequences of drink."

One marvels at the insight and sagacity these prophets displayed. How could these holy men so well
understand the facts of life? Another view of them will
help to explain:

The most awful feature of these times is witnessed in
the intemperance of the prophets and the priesthood. Even
that sacred office was profaned through the influence of
strong drink. The priest and the prophet have erred through
strong drink, they are swallowed up of wine; they are out
of the way through strong drink; they err in vision, they
stumble in judgement. For all tables are full of vomit and
filthiness, so that there is no place clean.

It appears that successful prophets in any age can
always use firsthand, inside information.

Other than providing a background on which to
hang the story of modern drinking, this seven-league-
boot history attempts to make the point that if there
is any change at all in drinking uses and abuses, manners and customs, it is microscopic. Humanity generally
has felt as did an ancient poet:

That poignant liquor, which the zealot calls the mother of sins, is pleasant and sweet to me. Give me wine! Wine that shall subdue the strongest, that I may for a time forget the cares and troubles of the world.

Herodotus writes of the Persians that they took care never to discuss important affairs of state unless they were under the influence of some wine. Why was this? Perhaps they thought it was a guarantee of a truthful approach to the problem in hand. As an old German proverb states, "In water you may see your own face, in wine you may see the face of another."

Or as Horace said, "Bacchus opens the gates of the heart." Can anyone produce a great line of verse in praise of tea or coffee or water as a drink?

Pure water is the best of gifts that man to man can bring,
But who am I that I should have the best of anything?
Let princes revel at the pump, let peers with ponds make free;
Whiskey or wine or even beer is good enough for me.

Advocates of abstinence have been embarrassed by the Bible. "No longer drink only water," Timothy was advised, "but use a little wine for the sake of your stomach and your frequent ailments." In fact the Bible suggests that wine is a gift of God; refers to bread and wine as staples of the diet; it includes wine as a measure of hospitality, and of value as a medicine and anesthetic. The most serious blow of all to abstinence-seekers may be the description of Jesus as a wine-drinker and changer of "water into wine at the wedding in Cana."

Other early references to drinking show that the ancients drank when they wanted to — and they often wanted to. They drank to reconcile enemies, to form family alliances, to elect chiefs, to stimulate debates. Tacitus wrote of the Germans that "the pleasures of the table expand their hearts, and call forth every secret. On the following day the subject of debate is again taken into consideration, and thus, two different periods of time have their distinct uses; when warm, they debate; when cool, they decide."

They also drank early to each other's health. This, the custom of the toast, is supposed to have been introduced by the hard-fighting Danes when they invaded the British Isles (toasts are mentioned in the Talmud). These haughty conquerors would not allow an Englishman to drink in their presence without special permission, death being the penalty. They meant it, too, as the Englishman knew so well that even when permission had been granted he preferred not to take a chance on a misunderstanding until the Danes had pledged themselves by raising glasses and expressing interest in his continued good health.

Men continued to drink through prohibitions, through times of plenty, through famines, through peace and war. They drank more under conditions of luxury than poverty, not so much because they had more idle time for drinking as because they had more idle time for thinking. The incidence of eras of debauchery rises and falls in correlation to conditions of emotional and social stress, of which luxurious pursuits are simply another symptom. One of the sharpest rises of intemperance, for example, occurred simultaneously with the beginning of the Christian era. It would seem inadvisable, if moderation is the aim, to load mankind with moral obligations greater than his capacity. Moral obligation beyond capacity and a rise of intemperance are not correlated by moralists, however; they prefer simpler explanations. The rise in drinking under Christianity, they say, came about because wine "has always been necessary for the most solemn sacrament of the Church." This must have been some powerful vintage of wine long forgotten, for that tablespoon of wine, indulged in only a few times a year during religious ceremony, could produce revelry and inebriety down through the Middle Ages.

Then, as now, simple answers did not solve complex questions. There was too much large-scale vine growing. By the end of the first five centuries of Christianity, when that religion was established by law as the religion of the Roman Empire, vine culture had spread throughout Gaul, and the church was preaching and planting at the same time. In this way originated some of the most famous present-day vineyards in France. Architects continually decorated churches with massive clusters of stone vines, and there is ample proof that substantially more wine was produced in those days than could have been consumed at the most frequent solemn sacraments.

And there were the feasts — Christmas, Shrovetide, Easter — which rapidly grew in number. Historical descriptions place them in a more raucous category than any of the ancient pagan parties, and considerably more compared to a modern New Year's Eve. For one thing, our clergy today do not usurp the role of ringleaders at these functions, and for good reason: they are not exposed as much. The reader must remember that monasteries were a species of public house in the Middle Ages and all travelers were well entertained there. The canons of some churches commanded their priests to practice this sort of hospitality, and one account says that "such hospitality led to scenes of excess."

Fairly strong language, but not strong enough. King Edmund I attended a feast at Puckle Church, Gloucestershire, in A.D. 946 and was there murdered. William of Malmesbury has described the brawl, explaining that the king and his courtiers and all his nobles were so drunk they could offer no resistence. William did not touch on the whereabouts and condition of the men of the cloth while the king was being killed.

The Archbishop of Sens, who lived many years later, writes more specifically of another occasion. The medieval "Feast of the Ass" was held in various parts of France and its ceremonies are described as impious (another outstanding understatement). Here is the recording:

The priests entered the choir besmeared with lees of wine, dancing, and singing profane songs, while the inferior officers of the church polluted the altar by playing cards upon it, and eating in the most disgusting manner. During the celebration of mass, old shoes were burned upon the censer, instead of incense, and the deacons and their companions were afterward carried through the streets in carts, practicing various indecencies. For several days, the most disgusting and extravagant actions were continued, and drunkenness and wanton singing universally prevailed both among the clergy and the laity.

These scattered examples inadequately represent the extent of medieval drinking. There are books full of them. Individual places and occasions among the ancients were often more eyebrow lifting, but for consistent heavy drinking the Middle Ages are tops. The clergy set the standard for the people and the clergy had the money and the wine. The strongest wines were even called by the name "theologicum" and the laymen who had the pleasure of drinking theologicum were beholden to the parish parson. He could afford to keep large groups so beholden. One reporter discusses a region which was less dissolute than the others and proves it by the statistic that the annual amount of beer malt used in an individual abbey was only nine thousand bushels. Logically, this was in addition to the wine, necessary to the most solemn sacrament.

The profession of religion has not been so intimately associated with drinking in more modern times, and the price of liquor has gone up. Perhaps the quality has gone up too. In eighteenth-century England liquor signs read: "Drunk for a Penny, Dead Drunk for Two-pence, Clean Straw for Nothing." Smollett enlarged his literary output by the following comment: "They accordingly provided cellars and places strewed with straw, to which they conveyed those wretches who were overwhelmed with intoxication. In those dismal caverns they lay until they recovered some use of their faculties, and then they had recourse to the mischievous potion; thus consuming their health and ruining their families, in hideous receptacles of the most filthy vice, resounding with riot, excretion, and blasphemy. . . ."

Yes, the old boys drank liquor. By some precepts they drank so much that the bud of civilization should have been destroyed. Instead, the impertinent bud presented them with straight alcohol.

Straight alcohol could have been anticipated. The recognition that there is something potent in wine which makes people feel better, vigorous, even younger, led to a search for the "spirit" of the wine. The isolating of this spirit resulted from first heating the wine while preventing the spirit's escape, and then cooling it to condensation. Thus, distillation was born. Since the spirit born of distillation was more potent and rapid in effect than in the original, diluted wine form, it was first used medicinally. Since it also made people feel younger, this led to the search for further spirits as the "elixir of life." Unfortunately there are those today who also use alcohol in this pathetic way to ward off the ravages of age.

As social revolution coursed along the path of history, alcohol gamboled alongside. The Industrial Revolution at the end of the eighteenth century spewed forth peaceful rural folk to devouring factory slums. Crowded, filthy and lonely, the exploited turned to cheap and potent alcoholic drink as the only sure and steady solace. The gin mills of English cities took their disgraceful place next to the mills of working death. While the upper classes sipped their vintage wine in genteel fashion to lubricate social ease, the lower classes swilled their beer and gin to drown their despair.

During this era of extremes, many cultured uses of alcohol were refined. The "dry" wine or aperitif (fifteen minutes before a meal) came into being. The light white wines with light foods, and the red full-bodied with the heavy, became the manners of taste during this period. The fractionated vineyard areas of France, Germany, Italy and Spain became renowned for the special gustatory delights each provided, and the seeds of status and culture were planted in the person who knew his wine. Although it was an age of strain, upheaval and rough drink, during the same period the relaxed, stable and delectable delight of good drinking for social benefit was refined.

The grapevine preceded Europeans to America. When Leif Ericson first visited the North American continent, he found vines already growing so luxuriantly that he called the area "Vinland" or "Wineland." It was so known in Norse literature for centuries.

Twenty-six years after the first voyage of Columbus,

Cortez, the Conquistador of Mexico, ordered that vine growing become an industry in the New World. Cortez stipulated that certain holders of land grants must plant, each year for five years, one thousand vines for each one hundred Indians living on the land.

The Jesuit fathers carried Spanish colonization and vine growing up the western coast into the Mexican peninsula to lower California, and their successors, the Franciscans, advanced into what is the state of California. As each settlement or mission was established, vines were planted as one of the first steps in transforming a savage wilderness into a state of civilization.

Anyone who looks at any drinking behavior in the United States has to look at our Puritan forebears. Too many of us accept the name Puritan literally, and assume that our early settlers were just that — pure. These hardy folk had fled what they thought was an irreligious, tyrannical and besotted land (and if you remember your history of England well you will recall that the Puritans were certainly correct about the last point!) and were, by the very nature of their exploit, inbred with reform. They were indeed brave, strong and determined — but they had less noble qualities as well.

For, strangely, after they had arrived on these shores they were not at all ready to abandon their liquor. Instead the Puritans gained a reputation for excessive devotion to drink. Their own writings indict them; their alibis and laws convict them. As a matter of fact, our Puritan forebears were continually ashamed of their drinking practices and busily blamed it all on their hard-drinking Anglo-Saxon ancestry, on their belief in the medicinal value of alcohol, and on the hardships of frontier life. As soon as they had settled they began to import wines and malts; then came the vintners and brewers, and before long the Puritans were experimenting with their own vineyards. Hard cider and applejack crossed their path rather early, but it was Jamaica rum that really whetted their palates.

Rum, a heady emissary of the first European settlers in the West Indies, took hold in the American colonies so hard that it appears to have been the loudest answer to Puritan prayer. It became, you might say, the mother's milk of this new nation. Its success was instantaneous, spreading with the force of a tidal wave. In short order, the manufacture of rum became New England's most profitable venture.

But as with many other highly profitable endeavors, it occurred at the bitter expense of others. The New England rum distillers succored the slave trade. Without New England rum the slavers of all nations would have been hard put to find a currency for their commerce. African slaves were sold in the West Indies for slave-produced molasses, which was brought to New England for rum. While we were getting wealthy, another part of the world was suffering separation, ignominy and inhumanity — which only serves to prove that things really do not change, do they?

For all the wealth and foreign suffering rum brought, it also brought something more. The receding tide of desire for it carried in a flotsam of regulations, punishments and hypocrisies. Soon, if his name was on the list, a rum-drinker could be arrested and fined, spend a sojourn in the stocks, lose his right to vote, or get publicly flogged and find himself in a criminal labor gang. But the tide and flotsam would not stop. Rum was too profitable; it was running all other liquors into the background. It flowed everywhere: in the finest and lowest taverns, in the finest and lowest homes. The tavern became the early rendezvous of judges and vestries, and almost no one complained when a group of Boston vestrymen requested that a tavern be opened next to the church for more ready accessibility. The ordinations of preachers, court sessions and town meetings were all occasions for heavy rum drinking. It was rum with sugar, rum with bitters, rum with sugar and bitters, rum with lime, lemon or pineapple juice, rum with bitters and juices, rum with sugar and bitters and juices, rum in flips and slings and punches, rum with honey and ginger. Or just plain rum. Indeed, if acquired characteristics could be inherited, the blood of Pilgrim descendants would show a high alcohol content.

Rum founded fortunes, expanded commerce, helped build the slave trade (as noted), enriched cities, and played an important role in the American Revolution. To be sure, the Puritans did not depend for long on the West Indies for anything as important as rum; they began to make it themselves. And, although the New Englanders never learned to distill it quite as well as the dark inhabitants of the sugar islands, they tried hard. They traded for molasses, and when the duty for molasses became too high they began to smuggle the rum in, which bothered the British customs a great deal more than tea. Soon molasses was being distilled to rum in homes everywhere, and shortly after each town had its own still house. In no time these town still houses were backed up by blossoming big distilleries in large trade centers throughout New England, New York and Pennsylvania, and as far away as the Carolinas. Newport, with some twenty distilleries, became rich on rum, and soon the beverage dominated colonial industry.

It is rum's association with the slave trade that is thought to have led to the expression "demon rum" used as an epithet against all liquor. I cannot help wondering, though, whether it was the rum that produced all the evil — or the fierce, unrelenting drive for profit and power which exploited rum.

Only the demand for a cheaper, more abundant liquor sounded the death knell for rum in the public's preference. Cheap American whiskey peeked into the scene in the border states among Irish-Scotch settlers to whom the making of whiskey was just another phase of farming. In time, the demand for home-made whiskey spread beyond the family circle, and the financial value of this sideline became apparent. Soon, the production of whiskey by farmers was so widespread that whiskey became the medium of exchange. The "hard" currency of that time was the strong sour-mash bourbon whiskey, which had taken over from rum as the most popular drink of the United States and maintains its position of eminence to this day.

The influence of the New World on history and its drinking pattern was soon felt. Fragile frontiers in an uncultured, unchartered, uncivilized milieu resulted in the misuse of alcohol. Potent liquor — readily manufactured, abundant and cheap — became the desire and its heightened rapid effects became the goal. Distilled hard spirits were sought; fermented gentle wines were neglected. Quick gulping took the place of relaxed wining. This rush toward effect robbed us of the real purpose of drinking, and soon all we could see were the *problems* of drinking, not the pleasures.

So much for history. Let us turn now to understanding; for if we understand we are not afraid — and therein lies the possibility of pleasure.

2

That Maketh the Heart Glad

THERE is no way to illustrate what liquor does to people without describing it technically. You probably are the rare one if you enjoy reading about the physiological and pharmacological effects of alcohol on the human body. Without enlightenment, however, the rich reward of understanding will pass you by. Some firsthand physiological and pharmacological knowledge you probably possess, but let us give you an objective perspective.

As anyone who cares to look at growing grapes can verify, their delicate skins are covered by a waxy film. Molds of yeast are deposited on this film when the grapes are gently kissed by wind and insects. Ten million yeast cells may be in residence on the skin of a single grape, more than one hundred thousand of a wine-producing type. These ubiquitous yeast cells produce their excrement-enzyme and convert grape sugars to alcohol. The great Pasteur showed that busy yeast organisms could convert even a simple sugar solution into alcohol. It was he who said, "Fermentation is correlative with life."

Beverage alcohol is therefore fecal matter. No grape or grain or other attractive flower makes alcohol. Rather, these fruits of the soil are devoured by the yeast, or ferment germ, and the germ then evacuates alcohol as its waste product. Shrink not from the thought. To be sure, the idea of consuming the excreta of a living organism does not tickle the esthetic palate of man, yet that is what people do — and with relish. You have probably used vinegar and yeast, eaten cottage cheese and drunk buttermilk most of your life. There is some slight comfort in knowing that the ferment organism is microscopic, but then oysters and clams on the half-shell are organisms large enough to be seen with the naked eye and we consume them — waste and all — by the bushel.

Alcohol is a snap to make. It owes nothing to man's creative hand, and will make itself if you let a watery mixture of vegetable sugars (fruits, molasses, potatoes, grain) stand in a vessel long enough. Spores of the yeast germ will fall into this food from the air and start eating, and excreting alcohol. In the course of its assault on these sugars, the fermentation germ repeats a cycle: yeast, like all living organisms, has only a limited tolerance for alcohol, and when that level is reached the yeast dies. By the natural action of yeast a healthy concentration of alcohol can be achieved. Moreover, the process can be hurried along by implanting spores artificially.

As noted in the historical section, concentrations of the important "spirit" factor can be achieved by way of distillation. Like the natural phenomenon of fermentation, distillation is a remarkably simple process: put the mixture into a pot with a spout and apply heat. You may remember from chemistry that alcohol is foolish enough to boil at a lower temperature than water; when one hundred seventy-two degrees is the temperature of the mixture, up the spout rush the alcohol vapors. But by cooling the spout, the rush is slowed and the vapors become fluid again, this time more heavily alcoholic. Repeating the process excludes even more of the water until almost straight, or pure, alcohol (ninety-three per cent, to be exact) remains. The perfectionist may wish to go higher in his concentration and, although it is difficult, it can be done.

Beverage alcohol measures its strength in so-called *proofs;* look at any liquor label. The origin of proofage, as with much that surrounds alcohol, is not easy to trace. Distilleries, which kneel at the altar of proofage, were unable to reveal where their deity was born. A hundred-year-old dictionary finally released the secret: it comes from "gunpowder proof." To test the strength of their liquor, early distillers would saturate gunpowder with alcohol and touch a light to it. If it flared up immediately, it was too strong; the proper strength would burn slowly in a blue flame. To achieve the desired effect, almost straight alcohol was diluted with an equal part of water. The resulting strength — half and half — was considered perfect, or 100 proof. It still is. Thus straight, or absolute, alcohol became 200 proof (which is not available since alcohol unfortunately dilutes itself from moisture in the air). The United States standard for neutral spirits is between 195 and 198 proof. Liquor sold in the United States has the proof-age on the label; divide this by two and you have the percentage of alcohol. For example 86 proof bourbon whiskey is 43 per cent alcohol. In the years immediately after the end of prohibition, a bartender could have diluted an open bottle. What stopped him was the fact that curious employees of the United States Treasury Department had the nasty habit of dropping in at irregular intervals and putting spirit hydrometers into random bottles. If the label read 86 proof and the instrument registered less, that place was no longer in business.

So much for what liquor *is;* now what does it *do?* This writer recognizes that alcohol is an ungrateful subject and people prefer their prejudices to understanding what it's all about. Let us try, however.

Liquor lifted to the lips, from the initial sniff, gets into the bloodstream in small amounts by way of the lungs. Most foodstuffs must wend their way down the esophagus and into the stomach, all the while undergoing chemical change but not being absorbed into the body until the small intestine is reached. Even water, the almost universal solvent, must wait until the large intestine. Alcohol is more versatile and ignores such restraints. Other foodstuffs begin to undergo chemical change in the mouth by the action of saliva and then are changed further in the stomach by its secretion; not so with alcohol. Saliva has little effect upon it and the stomach alters it little. *Alcohol is one of the very few substances absorbed into the bloodstream directly from the stomach relatively unchanged.* Fortunately, not all of the alcohol is absorbed here, for the effect would be heightened, quicker, and more dangerous. Twenty per cent may reach the blood from the stomach, but no more.

Strangely enough, this direct absorption from the stomach is a protective device; it prevents the drinker from being inundated. Coupled with this limited stomach absorption is the response of the stomach to irritants (if the reader will think about it, many of the pleasures of the body are a result of irritation). A muscle between stomach and small intestine closes down in spasm with continued irritation. Also, the stomach in self-defense secretes a mucous substance to soften the scratch of the alcohol against its tender surfaces. These two protective devices delay the passage of the alcohol into the small intestine, where no governor of rate of absorption exists and where all alcohol present is passed into the bloodstream. From the small intestine alcohol rapidly, constantly and completely moves on its inexorable course until no more lingers in the gastrointestinal tract. Indeed it is in such a rush to get into the bloodstream and is so diffusible that it can be recovered from all tissues, organs and secretions of the body moments after it has been swallowed. Incidentally, if you decided you did not like the

taste and only wanted the effect, you could have it in-
jected by rectum. But a word of warning: this less con-
ventional method will knock you cold from an amount
you'd barely notice if you swallowed it.

Now, aside from this first step of getting alcohol
going into the body, there is another point to be made.
We saw previously how the ferment germ excretes
alcohol until it produces a suicidal concentration. The
stomach, as noted, has flawless mechanisms for controlling how fast and how much liquor gets into the
bloodstream. But a drinker can respond *exactly like the
yeast germ;* by that I mean there is no protection
against the effects of a quick succession of alcoholic
drinks. Recently, a man at a bar wished to demonstrate
his drinking prowess; he would finish a fifth of whiskey
in six gulps. Not only did he finish the whiskey but
he finished himself, falling off the bar stool dead. He,
like the yeast, had created too high a concentration of
alcohol for survival.

We shall not provide the reader with a lesson in
anatomy by describing how the alcohol gets passed
through various organs of the circulatory system. What
we shall stress is that the entrance of alcohol is rapid;
its exit is slow. Here is one of the most important
points: *liquor is more intoxicating on its way in than
on its way out.* The effect is greater when the concentration is increasing than when oxidation is burning off
an equal concentration. Why is this important? The
susceptibility of beverage alcohol to oxidation is a distinctive and beneficial trait. Other forms of alcohol do

not leave the body as quickly as beverage alcohol and they accumulate to disastrous concentrations. Alcohol's ready combustibility (oxidation) makes it different from other foodstuffs which require extensive chemical manipulation before they are useful to the body. Beverage alcohol gets right where its going, makes its presence known, and thereafter gradually wends its way out.

Now the reason we stress that alcohol is much more effective on the way in than out is to benefit those of us who want to enjoy drinking. The myths are gone. Those who want to become intoxicated can learn how to do it. But there is something we'd like to emphasize: *the canyon between drinking for enjoyment and drinking to intoxication is as great as the chasm between social drinking and alcoholism.* Let us now explore the importance and significance of these differences.

Popular myths to the contrary, the drinker of liquor can do almost nothing to hasten the departure of alcohol from the body once it has gained entrance. He can, however, do a great deal about slowing the rapidity of absorption. Alcohol's chief deterrent to rapid absorption is food. No secret will be made about the importance of delaying absorption, but for the moment let us follow the swallowed liquor on its journey. In the stomach, alcohol is an innocent babe; but once it is in the bloodstream, its power is exerted. To all parts of the body it penetrates, and there it remains, asserting its influence until it has been completely oxidized and excreted. This is a process, by the way, which normally

takes place at a constant rate — whether you are playing tennis, resting in bed or talking hard — so there's
not much sense in trying to work it off. Time is what it
takes. Most other foodstuffs can be oxidized throughout
the body. Not alcohol; it is partial to the liver, where
most of its oxidation occurs. A healthy, intact liver de-
stroys alcohol at about one ounce per hour of 100
proof alcohol, a little less than the alcohol in an ordinary mixed drink.

Although alcohol reaches all parts of the body, including the bones, its most noticeable action is on the
brain. The experienced drinker and self-examiner
knows this well. Alcohol depresses the higher nerve
centers of the brain. It dulls the delicate functions of
the central nervous system, takes off the edge, and
makes drowsy the film of civilization which hundreds
of centuries have deposited there. Though it is endlessly
referred to as a stimulant, it is in no sense one. We
are talking now about how it *is*, not how it *feels*. Of
course the drinker feels stimulated, else liquor would
be unknown. But the truth of the matter is this: alcohol's drug action is anesthetic, causing progressive paralysis of the central nervous system — drink enough
and you will fall asleep; drink too much and you won't
wake up! We have all observed how one man can be
"tight" on one drink whereas the next man requires ten,
so there is no doubt about differing capacities. Experts
do not agree on the way this works, however. Tissues
are thought to build up resistance in seasoned drinkers;
also, oxidation is thought to be more rapid in certain

people, allowing them to drink more. Current thinking holds that either there is an adaptive increase in enzymes involved in alcohol oxidation, or new pathways are developed for the quicker removal of alcohol from the body. One feature of this capacity to tolerate a much greater quantity of alcohol is that it is reversible; many former consumers of a fifth find that two drinks are too much. Therefore, the safest way to remain a good drinker is not to prove it.

Of course, there is the psychological response to the effect by the experienced drinker. A practiced drinker surely remembers and recognizes his own familiar responses to liquor, certainly more than the nonpracticed. If the practiced drinker is drinking for pleasure and not for show, he should be able to avoid becoming his companion's responsibility. Just because he does not become so does not mean the liquor is not affecting him; else why would he drink? Poor drinkers do and say anything, have to be cajoled, pleaded with and taken care of, and then as a matter of course expect pardon the next day because they were drunk. If this is the way they want to drink, they obviously do not want to relate to you; they just want someone to look after them.

Take a close look at the eyes of a companion drinker you have to herd around; doesn't he seem to have plenty of awareness? Display annoyance or boredom and he will remember your behavior the next day. What he did or said himself are the things he cannot remember. Granted that anyone can make a mistake and have too much to drink; however, although we don't know where the drinker who aims for intoxication belongs, we are certain he does not belong on drinking parties.

The effect of liquor on your brain, of course, is easily discernible (and we will discuss this in more detail later on in Chapter 9). But the other organs are also being influenced, and we shall hastily allude to them. First, your blood pressure will increase — not from direct action of alcohol on your heart or blood vessels, but because of brain depression. The nerve center controlling heart beat has lost a bit of its authority and the heart beats faster, raising the blood pressure slightly. A fictitious sensation of warmth is experienced because the increased blood volume dilates the capillaries, reddening the body surface. (This dilation actually tosses off heat too rapidly, so liquor really causes a greater loss of true warmth than it supplies. Contrary to myth, it is an error to drink liquor during exposure to cold because of the rapid artificial lowering of body temperature. In other words, do not guzzle when you get caught in a blizzard.) Rest assured, however, that the vicarious effect of alcohol on blood pressure is too small to be significant and is directly related to the amount of liquor consumed. If you've been worried lately about your blood pressure and have been foolish enough to go on a binge, the next morning might be a comforting time to have your blood pressure taken. This leads to an admonition: *don't supply alcohol in conditions where the blood pressure has fallen.* And so, while it is always possible to dig up conflicting opinions on any subject, the general consensus is this: alcohol has no direct harmful effect on heart or circulatory system; it may even be beneficial.

The reader will remember that earlier we implicated the liver as the chief organ in the oxidation of alcohol. The liver is one of our best friends, but the worriers always believe that it is the scapegoat, taking a beating with every drink. Cirrhosis is supposed to be the result. Experiments have been (and continue to be) conducted to isolate the truth about liquor's effect on the liver. Although many bits and pieces have been fitting into place, the completed picture of the puzzle remains in doubt. One thing we are sure of is that segment relating to nutrition: the greatest enemy of the liver is nutritional deficiency, especially of the vitamin B complex. Although recent studies have shown how alcohol may cause acute fatty liver, *there is no available information to incriminate alcohol directly in cirrhosis of the liver.*

Next to the liver, the kidney is most suspected of alcohol injury, and with reason. The kidney is heir to more troubles than Job, and alcohol adds to them. A direct causal effect of alcohol on kidney disease, however, has yet to be shown. As to the urinary system in general, it would be hard to convince anyone who ever drank much that alcohol has no effect on urinary output. This annoying phenomenon is caused by the simple fact that alcohol suppresses the hormone that ordinarily holds back urine production.

In our day of scientific sophistication and worship of

the golden calf of science, we ought to wonder why mistaken images of liquor continue to stand. Perhaps the explanation is that while new knowledge is being gained, old knowledge is also being lost. Doubtless some lonely researcher has done the necessary study and published the work to remove the doubt. The results must have been delightfully interesting and spread rapidly by word of mouth. In the process, however, someone who was not listening got it backward and gave the wrong answer to five other people, who fanatically preached it as gospel to millions. In time, one half of the populace believed those who drank suffered no calamity, while the other half was equally convinced that they did.

At this point in time, the one man who had suffered for the answer was just a tiny burp in a sea of belchers. He probably died disappointed and despaired of leaving — instead of knowledge as his legacy — another unanswerable controversial question. The knowledge loss in the liquor story is a legacy of thousands of simple, unanswerable questions.

The main organs and functions of the body have all been described at one time or another as being eaten away, turned to stone, vulcanized, or otherwise fearfully attacked by liquor. The reader may be interested in the following quote by the clergyman Benjamin Parsons of the nineteenth century on the matter:

Among all sources of disease, alcohol stands pre-eminent as a destroyer. . . . This pestilent principle generally seeks for asylum where it may practice its deadliest deeds in some important and vital organ of the body. It sometimes makes the brain more particularly the seat of its venom, and victim of its cruelties. At another time, it hides itself in the inmost recess of the heart, or coils around it like a serpent; now it fixes upon the lungs; now upon the kidneys, upon the liver, the bladder, the pancreas, the intestines or the skin. It can agitate the heart until it throbs and bursts, or it can reduce pulsation until the brain sweats blood, and horrified reason flies away and leaves the man a maniac or a madman. . . . I never knew a person become insane who was not in the habit of taking a portion of alcohol daily.

With a brief bow to the sincerity of such reports, *there is no sound evidence whatsoever that alcohol causes permanent direct damage to the body.*

Lest it appear that I am heading toward the conclusion that alcohol is as harmless as milk, may I point out that alcohol, as almost anything, can have dangerous indirect effects. Much as this book wishes to orient the reader to the great majority of healthy drinkers and the pleasures of the vine, we cannot shut our eyes to the devastation from alcoholism — although the part liquor itself plays is indirect. As hinted above, liquor may aggravate existing kidney disease. Similarly, a troubled stomach with ulcer, an inflamed liver with hepatitis, the convulsions of an epileptic, all may be heightened by alcohol. But the direct creative or destructive power of alcohol, according to present knowledge, just does not exist.

Perhaps a quote will help: "There is a lack of evidence that either the temporary or prolonged use of alcohol, even in large doses, is the specific or sole cause of any disease." The author of that quote, the late Harrison Martland, was a pathologist of great repute who to my knowledge owned no stock in the liquor industry. Taken one step further, it is equally true to say that regular liquor drinking by a healthy, well-nourished individual in itself causes no direct disease. This statement is not to be construed as an inducement to uninhibited indulging, but as a statement of fact. If one chooses not to drink, he ought not to. The writer merely wishes to see that the choice is not based on myths and ignorance.

Let us now return to our look at liquor itself. It may be mere excrement to the yeast germ, but to us alcohol is like bread and meat, supplying energy similar to other foods. The only difference is that "liquor is quicker" — it supplies energy faster. Other foods are metabolized in fits and starts, while alcohol burns along at a constant rate to completion. Because liquor is used quickly and efficiently, while other foodstuffs mosey along, it is not used for tissue repair or for storage. Alcohol therefore cannot be stored as fat. Still, if you drink alcohol you *can* get fat. The reader will consider this a paradox. Not so. Since alcohol cannot be stored, it gets first chance as an energy-provider. This holds back on the energy to be provided by other foods, however, and, since they are not needed, they get tucked away as future energy in the form of fat. Alcohol is also generous in providing quick calories; an ordinary drink can provide about one hundred to one hundred fifty calories, and if you take enough of them to know it the next morning, you have probably had an extra meal — at least so far as food values are concerned.

This is discouraging, I'll admit, to those who like to drink a little and don't want to gain weight. Unfortunately, no factual solace can be offered (except that recently an effective reducing diet was suggested, whereby one glass of dry red wine at the evening meal was allowed). Moreover, if you cut down too much on other foods, you are liable to become intoxicated; and if you are a heavy drinker, and cut out nearly all other foods, you will get polyneuritis or Korsakoff's syndrome, which are even worse than they sound. The matter of fat is further complicated by the fact that liquor increases the appetite. This, by the way, is not due to stomach irritation creating a craving — alcohol by rectum will have the same effect. It is due to the brain center's lack of alertness in maintaining inhibitions — not for eating alone, but for all animal functions of the lower brain. Fatigue, jaundiced taste, dyspepsia and nervous indigestion, all are shunted out of the way so that not only does food smell, look and taste better, but gone is the will to resist it — a singularly bad situation from the waistline standpoint.

Although affluent societies are worried about obesity, the Mexican Indian, though poverty-stricken, is not malnutritioned — despite the fact that few of the foods considered good for nutrition are available. Tortillas are the first nutritionally important food the Indians have, followed by pulque, the bitter Mexican beer of the ubiquitous maguey plant. The rate of deficiency signs among pulque-drinkers is nine per cent, compared to forty-five per cent among the others. Don't tell the Mexican Indians that liquor is bad for them.

Beyond the nutritional benefits, mine workers in India find that during prolonged exertion a glass of country beer or country spirits is a good stimulant and restorer. In some mountainous areas where the people are poor and the climate harsh, the use of beer and spirits to tide over exhaustion after heavy labor has been known for centuries. All male and female workers in the coal-mining districts of Bengal and Bihar use moderate amounts of liquor, just enough to relieve fatigue and ensure a good sleep. Without liquor they could not go through the day, because their work is uninteresting and tiresome. Here, as elsewhere, the nutritive and vitamin values of liquors made from rice are substantial, and the nutritive value of native beer becomes an important part of an otherwise meager diet.

Alcohol, as we know, also aids digestion, but in a roundabout way. As the famous physiologist E. H. Starling once wrote:

Not only is greater enjoyment obtained from the meal. The enjoyment is due itself to the fact that alcohol has given him repose of spirit from the endless little worries of the day's work. He has sat down to dinner fighting the battles of the day over again, preparing for the work of the future, and seeking methods of warding off possible dangers to himself or to his plans. But for the moment these thoughts and cares are no longer of any value to him; the time has come for repose and repair; and to obtain complete digestion and assimilation he needs to free his mind of them. Under the influence of the alcohol past troubles cease to repeat themselves and to reverberate in his mind. The worries of the day fall off and he acquires rest and content, in which he takes a more sanguine view of the present and of the future, and leaves difficulties and . dangers till the morrow, when he will be prepared to deal with them refreshed and restored by the night's sleep.

We need no fancy researcher to tell us when we are worried or unrelaxed, or when the appetite and digestion are not what they ought to be. To come to the major meal of the day with a mind full of business matters and harassments is not conducive to a healthy life. Liquor is not the only method of interrupting the annoying trains of thought, but many a person is healthier today for having some liquor before dinner.

An important element in liquor's effect on digestion is *where* the drinking is done. The British pub is an excellent example of the social potential of drinking establishments. Working-class people can rarely meet in one another's homes for social endeavors as do the middle classes, and so the pub is the place where men meet other men, women other women. For the price of a drink, admission is allowed into this society; thus, for a pub-goer, drink is inseparable with socializing, relaxing and pleasure. Taverns have always served as meeting places for people who have no other. There a sense of belonging and a place in the community come into

being, and the lonely can achieve friendship and prestige during leisure hours.

Beer drinking once played a central role in ancient
Finnish society. Their sweet home-brewed beer was
regarded as a great delicacy in the time before sugar
was known as such. Hence, the beer barrel became the
center of festivals and merrymaking, the stimulant for
bards, the gravitational center for tax assessment meetings and the source for sacrificial drink.

The value of drinking places is further emphasized
by Vera Efron in her quote from *The History of Saloons*
by I. G. Pryzhov:

> In this kind of life, in pre-Moscow Russia (prior to 1450),
> there was no drunkenness. It did not exist as a vice
> gnawing at the people's organism. Drinking was glad-
> ness, pleasure, as is seen in the words attributed by an old
> Russian scribe to Prince Vladimir: 'Drinking is a joy to
> Russia, we cannot do without it.' . . . Around drinking man
> met man in brotherly fashion, man met woman, and held
> together by joy and love, the social life of the people
> progressed, brotherhoods sprang up, and the drinking
> house became the center of the community of each district.

Of course, when we talk about where we drink, we
ought to talk about feasting and partying. We fuss
about getting dressed up, putting on our best clothing,
washing behind the ears and round the neck, and getting there on time. When we gather around the drink
table, things are different. How essential a part of the
feast is the drink. What a beautiful procession drink

makes with dining, the liquor often so much better and more digestible than the food. How dull the dinner and party would be without liquor. And how the tongues are loosened, the hearts warmed, the better qualities brought out, enabling strangers to overcome shyness. And if the liquor is good, how well we all feel after it the next day, for good liquor and a good drinking experience are the best possible tonics. What incense is to a religious function, drink is to a festive occasion. It enables us to enjoy to the full, with all our senses and emotions, the good things which surround us.

Now to an important point of this book. Earlier, reference was made to the canyon that separates drinking and intoxication. Because we tend to focus on the problems associated with liquor, we have avoided the many instances where alcohol is useful. Those who have stressed the wrecked marriages, the quarrels begun or the business opportunities lost because of liquor have neglected to see the many marriages saved, the fights averted or the business opportunities gained thereby. Alcohol may create problems, but also solves and alleviates them. To drink, to enjoy, to live with liquor is for most an important experience. Why some would prefer to achieve drunkenness is not beyond the writer, but beyond the pleasure of liquor. So many of the scares, the innuendoes and the misconceptions about liquor stem from the fact that drinking and drunkenness are equated. *In fact, they are not the same thing.*

Socrates's comments about a symposium — a drinking

together — might apply today as well as to the yesterday when they were first delivered:

> So far as drinking is concerned, gentlemen, you have my approval. Wine moistens the soul and lulls our griefs to sleep while it also wakens kindly feelings. Yet I suspect that men's bodies reach like those of growing plants. When a god gives plants too much water to drink, they cannot stand up straight and the winds flatten them, but when they drink exactly what they require they grow straight and tall and bear abundant fruit, and so it is with us.

Drinking is a pleasurable partaking of another foodstuff, as an adjunct to the rest of the meal and the day's activity. Intoxication is a metabolic disturbance that can result from too much of anything. The two are not the same, and why we have had to frighten people about drinking via the excess of intoxication is strange indeed. No one suggests we ought to give up water, and yet too much water can cause intoxication and death. Oxygen is pretty important stuff, too, but an overdose of it can also cause intoxication and death; yet no one has suggested that we stop breathing it. *The person who drinks to get drunk is a fool and probably does not enjoy liquor anyway.* He likely drinks for oblivion, with alcohol only the means to attain it.

Possibly, as so often in human response, it is a question of climate, too. One needs to protect oneself against the hard winters and the heavy summers. Perhaps this is one reason why the Scandinavians have always been spirit-drinkers. As Saintsbury said, "I think those who can drink them [spirits] and do not, fools, but I think those who can't drink them and do, worse fools and unjust men too because they bring scandal on an excellent creature and consume that share of it that should go to others."

Therefore, if you would like to drink pleasurably and unafraid, put some physiological principles to use. There is a way to drink fairly consistently and remain perpendicular, mentally and physically. It can be fun, it can have certain social values, and it can leave you with pleasant, lasting memories.

Once alcohol is swallowed, there is only one place you can influence it: at the point of absorption. Recall for a moment the futility of trying to work it off. All the doctors in the world cannot retrieve it once the blood has taken it up. Oh, they may send you up in an airplane or ask you to breathe carbon dioxide, but these strenuous efforts will yield trifling results. The point of absorption is the only real chance. Since intoxication is greater during absorption, and alcohol is quickly absorbed, the trick is to slow the process down. Thus *dilution and food are your best bets*.

The matching of wines to food cannot be defended objectively. It serves only as a superstition of taste. There is some truth that red wines share with meat a complexity of taste and texture, and the high acidity of white wines may add spice to the blandness of fish (in earlier days, when refrigeration was unknown, the white may also have masked the odor and taste of decaying fish). Most likely, the wine-food pairing sprang from geographical considerations; that is, a wine grew in a region where particular foods were favored.

Along with dilution and food, timing is important. Suppose, for example, that you have had three or four martinis before dinner — the dinner will do little or no good in delaying alcohol's effect upon you. For remember, it is the time *before and during* drinking that is most important. All food markedly deters absorption; the alcohol becomes entangled with the food in the stomach and intestines and cannot as effectively reach the absorbing surfaces. The more food, the greater the entanglement. The amount alone is not the answer, however. Some food products have a greater affinity than others for impairing alcohol's rush to the bloodstream: milk, butter, cheese, meat, eggs — in other words, the protein foods. Complicated in their chemical structures, proteins digest slowly; alcohol entwined with protein is therefore delayed.

Water is the best of dilutants — not before drinking, but with or immediately after. Before drinking, water will wash the stomach's wall and facilitate the rush of alcohol into the bloodstream. But with or immediately after drinking, water will slow the process. We do not wish to belabor this point and bring in varying conditions. The point is that by using liquor sensibly with food and water one can drink, have the mild desirable effect, and avoid the unpleasantness of metabolic upheaval: intoxication.

The sensible use of liquor also requires leisure. Unfortunately, in most Western societies leisure is a thing of the past. Although we talk about it and plan for it, we do not know how to live with it. We rush, we gulp, we hurry. We wolf our food amid noise and clatter, we rush to work and then rush home or to the bar or to the cocktail party. There, all too often, the talk is abundant, but the communication is meaningless. One elderly colleague of mine, convinced that no one really listens at a drinking party, decided to test his thesis one night. Turning suddenly to a lady with whom he was conversing, he said: "I've just killed my grandmother." Her reply was a proper "Isn't that nice," and then she proceeded on her merry babbling way.

Rushing through our lives this way, unable to communicate, we drink under tense circumstances — with well-known disastrous results. Just as we no longer dine but eat, we no longer drink but gulp. Gulping drinks with little or no food, as we have seen, makes for heightened alcohol effects not of the most pleasurable kind. Conversely, have you not with pleasant, lingering memory and feeling recalled that delightful bottle of red wine and delicious meal you shared one relaxed evening with close friends? It was the sort of experience that can never result in unhappy episodes with liquor. As Brillat-Savarin said: "The discovery of a wine is of greater moment than the discovery of a constellation. The universe is too full of stars."

Conversely, can you not recall with displeasure the drinking party where there was naught but pushing and jostling, noise and clatter, mouths moving where people should have been, a pick of food and a gulp of liquid — perhaps too big a gulp too often? Is that the sort of experience of communication and living that provides pleasurable memories? Later on, when we talk about the whys and wherefores of drinking, we shall discuss how one method of drinking can make for health, the other for ill health.

Another popular myth is that liquor increases efficiency. Remember *alcohol relaxes*. The relaxing and narcotizing effect from small amounts of alcohol temporarily allows in some greater efficiency. But keeping this in mind, the truth is: if you perform anything better after drinking, from the crudest muscular effort to the most delicate thought process, you do it in spite of what you have drunk. You do not even sleep better after drinking — you are drugged, which is not at all the same as sleeping well.

The reader may readily ask at this point about all those energetic calories liquor was supposed to provide. Shouldn't they help increase one's operating efficiency? Unfortunately, the narcotizing effect of alcohol is greater than its caloric; brain and muscle are hit by alcohol simultaneously, but the brain is controlling. Although your muscles — and you — may indeed be tired, the narcotized brain gives a fake sensation of revival; you sense an ability to keep going only because the message your tired muscles are sending out is not being recorded accurately. (The same illusion occurs *without* liquor; any potent distraction from fatigue has a similar effect.) Accuracy suffers after drinking as well, although its unfavorable effects may be offset to some degree by the freeing of the mind from depressing distractions. In superficial routine it can aid concentration, but alcohol in reality has no valid role in work or function of most kinds. As someone has stated: "Alcohol can never make you do a thing better; it can only make you less ashamed of your mistakes."

Let us review for a moment: alcohol does not directly injure organs; it does not increase blood pressure; it does not make fat; it does not truly warm you. But brother, does it cause hangovers! Since the hangover is a question we are all concerned with, we ought to digress for a moment to examine it.

Let's put something to rest right now: *there is no cure for the hangover!* For the man who can come up with such a cure, all will be his. But for now, if you drink too much liquor tonight you will feel bad tomorrow. There it is. If you do not feel bad, then for you, at least, it was not too much. As for the accessory miseries (nausea, gastritis, anxiety, headache), they differ with the individual. But the main misery — the heart of the hangover, shared by all — is *fatigue.*

You have just seen how fatigue is produced by fooling your cerebral cortex. This is so important a point, let us take a moment to study it carefully. The body maintains certain protective warning devices: pain, fatigue, chills and fever. These, though discomforting, are essential for survival. Without pain a person does not know that an appendix is inflamed, a joint overextending, or a coronary occurring. Without chills a person is unaware that there is an imbalance of the delicate control of his body temperature, as fever also signifies. Likewise, fatigue should tell us that our nerves and muscles are tired, that exhaustion is around the corner. Now the reader will remember that liquor washes from the brain that film of reality which ordinarily alters the harmonious pleasure of being alive. Swept along in this wash is some of the brain's awareness of signals sent to it from the rest of the body. The depth of diminished awareness is related to the amount of liquor consumed and is intimately bound up with the mood and surroundings in which we have been drinking.

Also, recall that certain involuntary functions, such as heart beat, are speeded up when control is softened. Hence, on the outside we often push ourselves to the edge of endurance — by walking, dancing, standing, doing — while on the inside the certain involuntary functions race us on their merry way to fatigue. This powerful effect of alcohol in masking fatigue is one that fools us into believing liquor is a stimulant. In this hurried existence of Western societies, can you not see why our methods and places of drinking are the way they are? You are tired after working hard at a job in which you're not really involved (for a boss who is obviously not as smart as you), doing something routine, uncreative and usually highly pressured. By the time you get home, after fighting the angry driver or the elbowing commuter, your wife will probably be irked about something because she's tired, too. Isn't it better to dash off to a commuter bar or a cocktail party and gulp some liquid anesthesia? After a while, no matter if you're tired, bored or in trouble, you won't know or care about a thing! Just remember, however, that retribution is just a swallow away, because when you stop, as you must, the brain — fooled by alcohol — will revert to its former state and the pain and discomfort will return.

Now that you know how tired you really are — and how horrible that terrible reality — you have a choice: take another drink (to keep your brain off the job a while longer) or accept the inevitable. True, there are certain practical aids — not many, but a few. The best way to go about it is the preventative way: space *properly diluted* drinks apart and drink them slowly, with plenty of food in the stomach, some good, relaxing company, and about eight hours of sleep afterward. Do this, and you will not need to be concerned about hangovers. Remember, anything that helps you get rest is to the good; anything that interferes with sleep is to be avoided.

The "morning-after" headache is also the result of fatigue. The stress of being interesting, entertaining and alert while drinking in uncomfortable surroundings and with uncomfortable people is ultimately responsible for the headache, not the amount of alcohol or the minute vessel dilation which alcohol causes. A common myth relating to hangover horrors is that if the drinker had not mixed his drinks the night before, the disaster of the new morning could have been avoided. Let us bury that one. There is not a shred of evidence that changing what you drink — from whiskey to wine, or bourbon to scotch, or soda to ginger, or bitters to quinine — has any physiologically deleterious effect. Of course, your psychological expectancy of becoming ill from switching may prove yourself right, but that's another matter. As I have already pointed out, liquor will most often provide the effect that you consciously or unconsciously desire. The amount, type and location of the drinking may only be aiders and abettors to your anticipation. My dearest friend avoids martinis, which she loves, because gin gives her a headache. But I have seen her receive nothing but kindness from gin and tonics on many occasions. She is not alone in receiving from liquor what, at that moment, she expects it to give.

As for "hangover thirst," I need not describe that fierce, relentless, and unquenchable desire to those who have suffered it. Although alcohol is an astringent on the outside, it does not, contrary to belief, "dehydrate" the body when swallowed internally. That desert-like thirst we dread so comes from a physiological shift of body fluid from the cells to *extra*cellular areas; thus, regardless of the amount of water in the body, this lessening of fluid in the cells will produce insatiable thirst every time.

There are other hangover ills, of course, and they arise from a myriad of sources, not all understood. The type of food one eats, the type of liquor one drinks, the congener content (congeners are the extra-alcohol products produced by fermentation and aging) and other subtle influences, either singly or combined, produce the miseries of the morning after. Various distilled spirits, we know, can metabolize at different rates depending upon their congener content; apparently the action of some of the congeners is to slow up the rate of metabolism of alcohol in the body.

So count the hours. Time, a twenty-four hour abstinence, and perhaps a little aspirin are your best friends.

If you've gone this far, you already know a great deal about a substance we all live with, whether we drink or not. You know that alcohol does not cause disease or injury directly and that its many influences are exerted on the brain and central nervous system. This swathing of the brain and its dulling effect produce indirectly the pleasures and problems of liquor. Knowledge and experience with alcohol can provide for the drinker the only safe method of judging what to expect and what to avoid; and for the nondrinker, the same knowledge will allow for an understanding that can prevent the perpetuation of myths and misconceptions harmful to those who do drink. But whether one drinks or not, the important thing is *how* one drinks — and how he permits *others* to drink.

3

For Medicinal Purposes Only

NOTHING is easier to provoke than a prejudice and nothing dies with greater difficulty. Liquor, alas, has generated such a mass of them that even the smallest good word on its behalf sounds unreasonable. As you have already observed, it is my contention that alcohol may have been partly responsible for the start of civilization as we know it; it has been related to victories in war, even as used by the Lord; and, in spite of dire warnings to the contrary, *it does not directly cause any known damage to the body.*

Now even I must admit that this last clause looks strange on paper. We have all heard countless times about the evils of liquor, and we have also heard it intimated that alcohol is bad for the young and is a substance, if used at all, for adults. Nevertheless, we know of no evidence which suggests that alcohol is more harmful to the growing structure than to the fully grown. This latter point has been tested for generations in wine- and beer-drinking countries and ought to be considered proven. As a matter of fact, a British dental survey had the effrontery to state that beer was good for the teeth. After soaking young, healthy teeth in fourteen different solutions, including beer and fruit juice, the surveyors found that after six weeks the teeth in fruit juice had cavities, while those in beer were good as new.

Alcohol's general position in medicine dates back to antiquity. This should not be surprising since it is a common solvent in the preparation of standard drugs and is, of course, a drug itself. Further, alcohol is a foodstuff supplying energy faster than any other food. To my knowledge, it is the only substance in medicine which has both a drug action and food value, and which can provide energy and sedation simultaneously. The energy that alcohol provides is at a minimal cost to the body since it does not require digestion. Also, as a result of liquor's effect on the antidiuretic hormone of the pituitary (see previous chapter), alcohol acts as a *de*toxicant by ridding the body of poisons through increased urinary flow.

All of this is common medical knowledge and sounds very good. And yet, alcohol is rarely used by modern-day healers. Why should this be?

Unfortunately, in this day and age of highly specialized, impersonal medicine, physicians are pushed farther and farther away from knowing their patients as individuals by the increasing dependence on technology. The doctor relies more and more upon the advice of drug salesmen and the flood of advertising material which daily deluges him in choosing the drugs he will use. Because of this fact, many useful medicines slide into disuse while others less valuable are sold by the carload. The physician, therefore, wittingly or unwittingly, prescribes not necessarily the best drug for the patient, but the one he has been told is the best.

There was a time when getting the medical profession to accept a new medicine was a slow and arduous task. Not so today. An excellent, well-financed crash program of advertising and promotion can quickly lead to a new drug's use, with rich returns to its innovators and exploiters. It is the drug's economic and patentable potential that results in its push as a useful drug in medicine. For example, nicotinic acid, which was discovered in 1867, is not patentable and is in little use. Although known in the treatment of pellagra, it may also be useful in lowering blood fats, thus preventing some of the ravages of coronary disease. And yet, rather than promote this drug the promoters push instead more expensive but seemingly less effective products.

Our mutual friend, liquor, falls into the same limbo. Although our distilleries and wine merchants advertise their wares in highly selected media of advertising (not exposed to children, hopefully), no drug salesmen or advertisers stalk the physician into his medical lair to espouse the effectiveness of alcohol for the ill, aged and infirm. Without this constant pressure, and for other reasons as well, liquor has fallen from the list of medications doctors often use and is rarely mentioned in books on therapeutics.

There are other reasons, of course, why alcohol is unacceptable to the modern physician. He will tell you, for example, that he is afraid that continuous high doses of alcohol will produce symptoms of withdrawal, much the same as the effects from narcotics which are so well known to lay and professional reader alike. But narcotics and alcohol are not alone in producing this phenomenon: barbiturates — dispensers of drugged sleep — can also produce violent convulsions on withdrawal, as can some of the ubiquitous tranquilizers. And so doctors prescribe and pharmaceutical houses thrive. Narcotics, barbiturates, tranquilizers, liquor, water — they can all produce harmful results, but their proper use far more often than not is of benefit to man.

Prohibition also plays a role in physicians' disenchantment, medicinally speaking, with liquor. During periods of prohibition, the physician provides a legal means of procurement. Healthy friends and well-paying patients forced the doctor of the "dry days" to prescribe liquor as he now does tranquilizers; then, following legalization of liquor sales, guilt led him to prescribe it rarely — if ever — again. And, of course, there is personal prejudice, which probably plays a more important role in the elimination of liquor from its rightful medical role.

In any case, liquor as an effective therapeutic agent has become much misapprehended. Why? First, look at four conditions under which alcohol is frequently used by laymen for medicinal purposes: shock, snake bites, fatigue and colds. Really, it would be difficult to hit four other conditions for which liquor is *less* desirable. You will recall that alcohol lowers blood pressure; so do shock and snake venom. In fatigue, we have already seen how liquor lulls the brain into falsely interpreting the signals from the muscles and nerves so that we know not how really tired we are. And as for colds, they require rest and a stable body temperature — alcohol, remember, will not let us respond to fatigue messages and raises surface temperature while lowering the body temperature.

On the other hand, gather together a group of laymen, and they will look with horror at the thought of using liquor in the treatment of heart disease, cancer, malnutritioned alcoholics with liver disease, and diabetes (these and other conditions we shall presently touch upon). Now here is the constant paradox this book seeks to expose: that of problem "tails" wagging socially useful "dogs." For example, you have just read about the dire results of drinking liquor for colds. Nevertheless, taking a hot toddy at bedtime with a resulting beneficence to a cold does not refute anything just written. And while it is true that liquor will increase fatigue because a drugged cerebral cortex has allowed some internal mechanisms to race ahead, nonetheless this same drugging will also relax congested air passages and thus permit easier breathing, dull a sense of discomfort, and help achieve a better night's sleep.

Liquor has the ability to produce a rise in nasal temperature and it is this action that underlies the physiological usefulness of alcohol during the early stages of a common cold. The decreased blood flow and resulting low supply of oxygen which follow chilling of the body surfaces injure nasal defense mechanisms and help pave an easier road for acute infections. Vasodilation produced by liquor reestablishes circulation in chilled cutaneous and mucosal surfaces and makes them less liable to infection. This effect, in addition to a feeling of comfort which liquor provides, induces drowsiness and thereby promotes a desire to rest.

Thousands of years of trial and error have built up a long list of uses for liquor in medicine. As Salvatore Lucia has said, "Wine is the oldest of medicines." Medicinal salves made with wine were used in Sumer as early as the third millenium B.C., according to tablets found in the ruins of Nippur, and virtually all cultures at one time or another used wines for medicinal purposes, directly or as a solvent. However, this book is not intended as a guide for self-treatment, since even the physician who diagnoses and treats himself is considered to have a fool for a doctor. So the use of liquor as a medicine does not imply that we should help the bartender close the place or keep a bottle tucked handily in the desk drawer.

But there are paradoxes: on the one hand, we know how the use of liquor in infection can be harmful; but on the other, we also know how the use of liquor in infection can be *beneficial*. A common infection known from ancient times is gonorrhea. Now a guiding principle of medicine which still persists in the treatment of any infection, despite the advent of antibiotics and other fancy medication, is that of rest — rest in general and rest for the infected or injured parts. We know that liquor can both increase fatigue and cause increased urinary output, thus making the infected area in gonorrhea work overtime. Therefore, sensibly and correctly (the two are not mutually inclusive; sometimes we can see what is sensible and still do the opposite, which in the pursuit of pleasurable living is correct), liquor is not indicated in the treatment of gonorrhea.

But a patient is feverish from an acute infection; and although we have many chemical cannons to shoot at the patient, let us for the moment focus only on liquor's role. Some will question whether or not alcohol increases susceptibility to infection, or lowers or raises resistance. In a patient already infected, these are academic moot points. The truth of the matter is this: the patient is uncomfortable, apprehensive, restless and without appetite; nourishment is necessary but ordinary foods arouse naught but nausea in the patient. Intravenous feeding, although certainly effective, is at best a worrisome, annoying procedure. But supposing his enlightened physician prescribes carefully controlled doses of alcohol. He knows at what rate the patient can oxidize alcohol; therefore he can avoid building up a level to create the metabolic disturbance of intoxication. By maintaining a low rate of administration, a small amount of alcohol is put to work but the accomplishment is notable. In the course of a waking day a patient could well be fed one hundred seventy cubic centimeters of liquor and, with proper spacing, not a symptom of intoxication will appear. This small dose of liquor, however, will provide well over a thousand calories, which is half the daily requirement of a person at rest in bed. Even though the patient may not realize he has had much to drink, his brain and nerve centers do and he is consequently more relaxed, less fretful, and, calorically speaking, nourished. Moreover, his infirmity seems less alarming, not only to the patient but to those around him. His neighbors look more interesting — and they, in turn, are more interested in him.

Furthermore, liquor does not have the unpleasant or dangerous side effects of other drugs. Antibiotics have surely been a great blessing, but as with alcohol, too much of a blessing can be disastrous. Antibiotics are used too early and too often, and we may in time pay the price for this free and easy use. On the other hand, liquor in small doses as food and sedative is old stuff with doctors (even though it no longer is fashionable).

There are some, of course, who will say that tranquilizers are better. This, too, is a matter of opinion. Tranquilization can lead to a deadly vegetable-like existence: easy to manage, but not much alive. This automatous, pleasureless existence may be the goal of some, but I prefer for myself (and my patients) a bit of pleasurable living instead. Of course, I am realistic enough to realize that if the proper, controlled used of liquor came back into the practice of medicine, the sale of tranquilizers and many other drugs would plummet. Other considerations aside, liquor in small, controlled doses can safely be used; for example, as an analgesic for minor pain, as a tranquilizer or sedative, as a vasodilator, as a diuretic, as a nutritional supplement, as an aid to absorption of fat by the intestines after surgery for ulcers or stomach cancer — and as you shall see shortly, as a social lubricant for patients on chronic-disease wards.

Kidney trouble is another ailment universally thought by laymen to be a contra-indication to liquor use. Most likely this myth grew out of the erroneous belief that alcohol causes kidney disease. On the contrary, alcohol, with its strong affinity for fats, is little attracted to kidney tissue because of the low fat content of this organ. In Bright's disease, a kidney ailment of serious proportion, a monotonous low protein, high carbohydrate diet is often essential. Here again, liquor can make the patient's diet more attractive, while at the same time providing needed nourishment. Thus the Bright's disease sufferer avoids consuming protein — which for him is deadly — while at the same time his caloric needs have been supplied via liquor.

What has just been said for Bright's disease can be said for other ills as well, even those of most serious consequences. In high blood pressure and heart failure, for example, where a low-salt diet is important, low-salt wine and whiskey can make mealtimes infinitely more pleasurable. The palatability of beer, its mild alcoholic action and the feeling of enjoyment which it provides, make it suitable for inclusion in restricted diets; its sodium content, moreover, is less than that of many foods prescribed in low-salt diets. We physicians are constantly devising and utilizing new scientific measures to prolong life, and yet we avoid consideration of those factors which make it worth prolonging. A colleague of mine in his late eighties suffered a mild heart failure and was immediately — and correctly — placed on a salt-free diet. This doctor had lost his family and his friends and had little reason for joy, but he tried to maintain his good graces and not burden others with his years. An acquaintance visited him one day and brought along the patient's favorite food: a hot pastromi sandwich, rich in flavor and salt. What a dilemma! On the one hand, the need to adhere to a correct medical regime; on the other, the chance for a few moments of pleasure and satisfaction in an otherwise drab life slowly ebbing to its close.

"Shall I, or shall I not?" asked the physician. No man can, or should, answer such a question for another unless he is vested with the robes of deity. As it happened, our colleague lived for many years beyond that sandwich and both he and his physician shared the satisfaction in knowing that, whatever the outcome, at the proper moment obeisance had been given to *living*, not to longevity.

Liquor as a medicine for the treatment of heart disease has been of value for centuries. The gripping clutch of painful angina pectoris was eased by alcohol long before newer medicines came upon the scene. Not only is alcohol important in dilating the heart's own blood-vessel system at times of painful stress, but the anxiety-provoking terror of the cardiac cripple awaiting the next attack can be lessened by carefully controlled and spaced doses of liquor. Remember, for the cardiac liquor acts as a sedative, it supplies energy, and by its action upon the brain it produces relaxation and dilation of the circulatory system, thus allowing the blood to flow more easily to the draught-ridden heart muscle.

While I am at it, let me strike at one further myth: that hardening of the arteries is caused by drink. In spite of accumulated evidence to the contrary, this particular fantasy clings on. Pathologists — those medical detectives of the dead — tell us *there is no evidence to incriminate alcohol in the inexorable process of narrowing vessels.* Because of the vasodilating effects of alcohol and its strange attraction for fats, some daredevils go so far as to say that alcohol may even foreclose rapid hardening. No one to my knowledge has yet suggested using liquor as a prophylaxis against arteriosclerosis; about that we cannot yet say. The fact is, we do not know what the normal amount of hardening is for any individual at any one time.

We ought to turn now to a discussion of liquor in chronic and terminal illnesses *without* cure, such as cancer and uremia. We scientists of the body have lovely methods of intravenously balancing body fluids and chemicals — all very scientific and correct. Why not provide such terminal cases with liquor — under careful supervision, of course — and ensure a few days of less tortured life (and indirectly help those around as well)? For the attitude of the sufferer burns deeply into the emotions of loved ones who must helplessly watch the agony. The gentle facade that liquor can drape over the dying — of benefit to patient and family alike — is not unlike the drape of senility nature provides to ease our passing from the scene. We should be reminded of the biblical statement, "Praise to God who brought forth food out of the earth, and wine that maketh glad the heart of man."

This raises another issue of increasing importance to users of liquor, concerning the most common prolonged illness known: incurable, inevitable old age. Hardening arteries, faulty digestion, insomnia, generalized aches and pains, feelings of uselessness, all are the symptoms of the elderly. My grandfather, who is eighty-nine, has suffered all of these pangs at one time or another, but on those occasions when he has dinner at our house he always leaves in good humor, having charmed us with his reminiscences and thoroughly enjoyed himself. His circulatory complaints disappear, his appetite, digestion and mood are excellent. Sleep, after such an evening, refreshes him. The reason: one whiskey before dinner and a scotch after. This is all that is necessary to produce what his nurse later reports as a "miraculous change." Getting out to see his family helps, of course, but so does the liquor. You see, at home he cannot have it — because his nurse is afraid he will become dependent on it!

Patent-medicine makers have also learned the value of alcohol. They know, as did the itinerant medicine man of the previous century, that the potency of their product depends solely upon alcohol. A maiden aunt of mine, who would fear she'd been soaked in the brine of the devil if ever she partook of liquor, swears by a rejuvenating tonic she once saw advertised on television. Prior to taking this cure-all, auntie, was feeling pepless and blue, old and discouraged, lifeless and unrelaxed. But, now she attests, "It's made a new woman out of me!" She has pep galore, boundless enthusiasm, a younger and more hopeful outlook on life. I haven't the heart or sadism to tell her that it is her ancient enemy, liquor, that has given her this new-found bounce; that the splash of new life on her formerly drab existence has been painted by alcohol; that the flight of her aches and pains was strictly liquor-induced (I don't have to be afraid auntie will read this book and learn the truth, either, for her antipathy to alcohol extends even to great displeasure that her nephew does his work in the field!).

My aunt is not alone in her response. I have a colleague whose "grandpappy" was a traveling Baptist preacher, and you can guess how he felt on the subject of liquor. During his religious travels, however, repayment for whatever divine incantations he might render was usually tendered by a big dinner. Now one devoted parishioner had a favorite ham-sauce recipe, which she made with lots of sherry. The preacher devoured much of this gourmet delight, and, as his stomach expanded and little room remained, he was asked by his hostess if he cared for more ham. "No, ma'am, thank you," he said. "But I sure would love some more of that delicious, wonderful sauce of yours!"

As did my aunt and my colleague's grandfather, so do many others deceive themselves in relation to liquor. They decry and avoid it on the one hand; but when deceived, they enjoy its benefits to the fullest.

If the goal is to make old age a period of penitence and regret, then I say — let's deny them liquor. Many elderly people are full of regret. Life has rushed by them while they twiddled with nonessential details. They followed all the rules, played it safe and achieved longevity — and yet that horrible empty sensation of life having skipped by pricks at their senses. Because of their conditioned attitude toward liquor, however, they cannot now take the initiative — someone must prescribe it for them. Let the physician take the blame! Thus, a glass of wine with lunch and dinner, a highball before retiring, and bleak, tired eyes become magically brightened.

As for getting the "habit," you had better worry more about morphine or the other narcotics they give you for your pain; you can get the "habit" much faster that way. (In recent times, pediatricians have supplied alcohol to infants and children in a variety of conditions without fear of habit formation; yet one would think that the young are the most susceptible to habit.) Recently an elderly gentleman, accustomed to some liquor each evening with his meal, became very upset upon being hospitalized without it. Uncomfortable, unhappy and uncooperative, he put up such a struggle that the daily ration was grudgingly provided; after that, he was a different man — but the hospital personnel were convinced he was now "hooked" on liquor. I sometimes wonder if the people who express such constant fears of someone "getting the habit" are not putting upon others their own hidden desires. Weep not for our patient who wanted his daily ration, for he is as much "hooked" as those who are addicted to eating three times a day, or sleeping a certain number of hours a night, or taking aspirins for headaches. Certain daily rituals simply become part of our way of life; to remove them creates a feeling of emptiness — but that does *not* mean being hooked, habituated or whatever else those riders of rigidity prefer to call it.

For years athletes in training have been admonished to avoid cigarettes and alcohol. I can certainly understand the rationale behind not smoking, because it impedes one's breathing capacity. I can also understand why the athlete, as anyone else, ought to avoid an intoxicating experience. But why beer, or wine, or spirits in small amounts cannot be served at the training table is beyond my understanding. All day long, the athlete in training must drive himself under physically and emotionally tense conditions. Then comes the evening meal, a little relaxation and an early bedtime. Why not some wine with the evening meal, or a highball before retiring? The relaxation and appetite stimulation which liquor can supply would be invaluable.

The Soviets have apparently not been restricted by such ancients myths; for their Olympic athletes, cases of Russian wine (not at all bad) are made available at the competition. Perhaps recent Soviet Olympic victories have been achieved not alone by subsidization "above board," but by liquor for relaxation on the dining board. In my opinion, it makes good sense. Furthermore, athletes are excellent ego-ideals for our youngsters and could effectively illustrate in practice that a little liquor can do some good — not necessarily some harm.

Perhaps the one remark that likely has tweaked your curiosity throughout this chapter is that one suggesting alcohol's use in the treatment of the malnutritioned alcoholic with liver disease. Everyone knows about the warning that an alcoholic better not touch alcohol or he'll be off to the races; well, on a damaged liver it is unthinkable. But is it? A small amount of alcohol administered with proper meals may actually *hasten* recovery in the hospital. That familiar, friendly substance, with its ready energy and its brightening of sickroom reality, certainly can do no harm. And those of you who fear that the taste of demon rum will set our patient off on a liquor binge are wrong: the properly cared for, hospitalized alcoholic rarely feels the tug toward alcohol while on the inside. Only on the outside, where his burning inner fears meet the cold outer realities, does he seek the solace of the bottle. So fear

not, brothers; a bit of healing comfort to the sick can
do no harm.

Liquor has surely been forbidden in patients recov-
ering from viral hepatitis. In a clinical study made by
the Armed Forces European Hepatitis Center, it was
concluded that "patients drinking relatively large
amounts of alcohol in the period of convalescence, six to
twelve months after acute hepatitis, showed no more
evidence of post-hepatitic liver damage than those who
consumed small amounts of alcohol or none at all."
Even in cirrhosis of the liver, where patients were studied with and without liquor during the convalescence
period in hospital, liver biopsy and chemistries revealed
no deleterious effects. With alcohol, the patients were
cooperative; they had good appetites, their liver size
remained the same or decreased. Even in patients with
peptic ulcer, alcohol is not definitely contra-indicated
unless the patient shows an increase in symptoms after
its use.

Another condition of deprivation, diabetes, requires
a word or two. For many years doctors have been telling their drinking patients with diabetes to give up
liquor. Many a patient has reported that his physician
told him: "Alcohol turns to sugar; you cannot have it."
As a physician, I know how often doctors are mis-
quoted; unfortunately, it is one of the reasons why they
have to be secretive and reticent about providing information. Having read in Chapter 2, about the creation
of alcohol, however, you know yourself that any solution of sugar can turn to alcohol, but not the other

way. Granted, there is still some controversy in medical circles about whether or not alcohol increases or lowers blood-sugar levels; this same controversy has led many specialists in diabetes to warn against the evils of drink, often in direct correlation to their own prejudice for or against liquor.

Today, if you should press an authority on diabetes about alcohol, most will admit there really is nothing wrong with alcohol use by diabetics *when under careful control.* This control must provide for the correct elimination of carbohydrates in order to maintain a proper nutritional diet. I am not — repeat *not* — pushing liquor in diabetes. But in a condition where the patient is deprived of much which is pleasurable in life, if small doses of liquor can lighten the load and provide a small increase of pleasure for those who prefer to drink, why not?

We have observed how liquor can serve as a nutritional supplement, how it can provide a heightening of enjoyment in lifeless diets, and how it helps lessen the harshness of reality. Let me elaborate briefly on this last point in terms of present-day doctor-patient relations. The modern physician is so specialty-conscious and has so many tests available to aid diagnosis that he focuses on symptom-removal alone and not on the effect of treatment upon the whole patient. Let me give an example. A physician suffering from Parkinson's disease was uncomfortable with the tremor and rigidity of his right arm. Nevertheless, with this impairment he continued to practice medicine and fulfill his responsibilities to himself, his family and to society. Neurosurgical colleagues, however, recommended a procedure to remove the annoying symptoms. Pre-operative psychiatric evaluation indicated that, for emotional reasons, surgery would be bad for the patient. Nevertheless, pressure from various sources in favor of surgery led ultimately to the procedure. Six months after the operation, the neurosurgeons reported an excellent response to the surgery: the rigidity and tremor in their colleague's arm were gone.

But what about the whole man? Following surgery, the patient never again returned to his practice of medicine. He became addicted to narcotics; he required constant companionship to guard against his impulsive suicidal tendencies; he suffered severe depression; and he was unable to fulfill any obligations to himself, to his family or to society. The annoying symptoms were gone and the operation had been adjudged a success, but in my view the procedure was a complete and tragic failure.

This same focus on symptoms instead of people has caused us to lose our perspectives. All treatment, all symptom-removal, we preach, must produce a positive response. It isn't necessarily so. Many a patient may be better off with an unhealthy symptom than be ruined by a cure. If a man wishes to risk becoming a smoking-cancer statistic rather than be a miserable, depressed, unhappy being, that should be his choice. If small doses of liquor can help make life more palatable, ease the weight of chronic pain or old age, and lubricate the adjustment to nagging illness and recovery, *why should it be denied?* Why can't the chronic-disease wards in our hospitals provide liquor in small doses to patients with evening meals, or perhaps schedule a cocktail period whereby the patients on the ward can chuck the deadly routine and socialize a bit? It would only help counteract the tendency in all chronic sufferers to withdraw into themselves and to become married to their bodies and complaints — and thus miss out on the benefits and lightness that can come from sharing a delightful moment with other fellow beings.

Perhaps by eliminating our ill-found prejudices and by considering the whole patient, perhaps a measure of peace and pleasure *can* be provided for some of the sufferers in our society.

4

Awake and Fill the Cup: Liquor and Sex

SINCE primitive times the customs and beliefs dealing with the liquor-sex union have abounded. The identification by certain primitives of intoxicating drink with human semen led them to believe that both were originators of sexual excitement and that both possessed life-giving properties. The legends involving the creation of Prometheus, that daring thief of fire from the Olympian gods, are often related to the drinking of the gods. In the Greek tales of the birth of the god of wine, Dionysus, the identification of liquor and sex is even clearer, not to mention the use of love-potions, those saturators of ancient legends that brought together drinking and sexual gratification. Countless other customs in the same vein have firmly established the relationship, as witness the following: the erotic nature of all the god-wine festivals; the equation of palm wine with breast milk; the belief that a palm planted by a woman yields more sap; the prohibition of sexual activity during wine making to ensure full potency of the drink; the ban on the sexually incapable or menstruating members of a tribe from making wine; the interminable list of customs joining drink and marriage ceremony.

It is time for a look at liquor and sex.

If you happen to be one of those rare people who have enough self-respect to pay attention to their own feelings and experience, many of the things I shall tell you will not be unfamiliar. For example, you know that liquor is a sex *depressant,* not a stimulant. You should also know that the feeling of stimulation is fictitious, physically speaking, and that in ample doses alcohol induces temporary impotence. You should also recall how alcohol narcotizes the brain and higher nerve centers, releasing inhibitions and inciting more animal-like behavior. In short, determination without ability is what happens when you mix liquor and sex, and it is this diad which causes such embarrassment and leads to so many ancient and sour protests. For this reason Shakespeare has his porter in *Macbeth* say:

[Drink provokes] nose-painting, sleep, and urine. Lechery, sir, it provokes, and unprovokes; it provokes the desire, but it takes away the performance. Therefore much drink may be said to be an equivocator with lechery; it makes him, and it mars him; it sets him on, and it takes him off; it persuades him, and disheartens him; makes him stand to, and not stand to; in conclusion, equivocates him in a sleep, and, giving him the lie, leaves him.

Shakespeare's observation describes a response as true then as always. In Shakespeare's day, in fact, there lived a gentleman with the charming name of Boniface Oinophilus de Monte Fiascone, who rebelled against his own family by writing a book praising drunkenness. In it he reminds us that "drunkards are not generally given to lewdness," and further emphasizes that "in those countries where they do not drink to excess they are very much addicted to debauchery."

But we are not confined to Shakespeare's time alone. Athenaeus reported that intoxication was the cause of Alexander the Great's weak inclination for women. And that erudite gentleman Aristotle, who once said that the semen of drunkards becomes watery, further remarked that "too much drinking makes one very improper for the acts of Venus." (Aristotle did not complain of another function of liquor, closely related and equally inevitable: its tendency to slow orgasm.)

Let us analyze why liquor fools you. The lower part of the brain receives all stimuli and bosses all animal functions: eating, drinking, speech, elimination, propagation and other biological activities. The most animal of us all, the newborn infant, wants to eat and drink whenever the stimulus strikes; he will holler and bellow until he is picked up and held, no matter what the hour; and he eliminates as easily and openly as the rain that falls. Only as time passes do parents and society interpose their rules and regulations as to how, when and where these needs are to be satisfied. The older we grow the greater become the restrictions and responsibilities until there evolves an adult who, under proper control, eats at certain times, in certain places and with certain instruments; who uses tact and accepted symbols of speech; who eliminates in proper places; and who certainly copulates only under legal and social limitations.

Man, we have noted, is the only animal with such an inner being controlling his own response to his own desires — and it appears he is not loath to dethrone it occasionally in order to stage a private revolution. Everyone has sexual thoughts and desires, and I mean everyone: priests, nuns, janitors, bankers, doctors, lawyers, school teachers, gas station operators, alcoholics, teetotalers, vivisectionists and antivivisectionists — everyone. We may not admit, or be aware of, the sexual impulse lurking within us, but we can be certain it is there. It must remain there, of course, since this desire for sexual union is what keeps the human race going. A friend told me of a confirmed teetotaler who was a guest at dinner, and who at the end of the meal was offered a glass of cognac. Proudly he proclaimed in a loud voice, "I would rather commit adultery than drink a glass of cognac." The ancient and revered father of the house broke the silence by saying, "And who wouldn't?"

Later on we shall, you and I, discuss sex in Western society at greater length. But first, let's get back to that small private revolution and our dependable conspirator, liquor, which can so quickly seduce and expand our egos. Impulse becomes master as restraint bows out, and all barriers — legal, moral and social — melt away. Like all conspirators, however, liquor in its alliance in the overthrow of controls displays a traitorous side — for we now have an expanded ego leading a sleeping army. No device is available to inform us of this development — only time. For, while alcohol has partially narcotized our nerve centers, its ability to distort reality has produced an irresistible sexual image of ourselves. We are full of ideas — a good many of them carnal — and it is a waste of time trying to convince anyone at such moments that liquor is not a true aphrodisiac. Only the next hour or two will tell us the sad truth.

Yet, you wisely say, how about that bar-and-brothel combination? The relationship between drunkenness and sex offenses? The lessened ability of the intoxicated to take proper prophylactic and contraceptive precautions? And what about intoxication and illegitimacy? Or the most famous saying of them all: "I wouldn't have, if I had known what I was doing"? Are these myths and misconceptions — or are they realities?

Myths and misconceptions they are not; realities they are. The pharmacological and psychological effects of alcohol are as stated — the only question is to what degree each works. In other words, *how often* do sexual blunders occur in proportion to the amount of inebriety? Most of us who were being honest would respond, "Pretty often," for the linkage of liquor and sex is inevitable.

We know, for example, that without liquor many a man would never have examined the inside of a brothel or have needed treatment for venereal disease, that countless abortions would never have been performed, that many a preposterous love affair would not have seen the light of day. But do we really know so much about liquor and love, blondes and bedrooms, martinis and marriage, that we need not explore the subject any further?

It may reassure you to learn that *most people will really not, under the influence of liquor, do anything they wouldn't do without it.* As we shall observe in a later chapter, the linking of events on a simple one-to-one basis is not the way things happen. The virgin who succumbs because she drank too deeply was tired of waiting *before* her first drink; that man who wanted to see what the inside of a prostitute's house looks like had his bulging eyes *before* the first swallow; the venereal disease sufferer was not too choosy an individual *before* drinking. And finally, bear in mind that abortionists have always thrived during dry periods as well.

Fundamentally, the point to keep in mind here is the similarity between drinking as such, and sexual activity as such. They are incompatible with one another — not because of the impotency response, but because the two compensate one another and, in one highly important area, they serve the same purpose: both provide temporary escape from controls; both have the power to seduce and expand the ego. During the Second World War, I worked in the venereal-disease unit of a large military hospital. My task, beyond giving the uncountable injections, was to learn under what conditions the infection was acquired. The material I gathered showed that only 10 per cent were drunk; another 18 per cent had taken some liquor but were not drunk. Of the remainder, 48 per cent were cold sober and 24 per cent were total abstainers! And remember, these data were collected by verbal inquiry, where we could have expected the invariable tendency to blame the misdeed on drunkenness — the "I'd never have done it if I hadn't been drunk" alibi. Yet, only 10 per cent claimed they were drunk and almost three out of four had been infected without *any* contact with alcohol beforehand.

Well, then, since contact with venereal disease is not augmented by liquor, surely prostitution is? Not necessarily so. Studies of imprisoned prostitutes reveal that many were nondrinkers before they began to ply their trade; they began to drink only because of the demands of the profession itself — that is, drinking helped them to get up their nerve to accost possible clients, or simply to put up with the clients. As Ovid, that highly polished Roman observer, concluded over two thousand years ago, women who sell themselves consume alcohol in large quantities not for pleasure but for narcosis. "All my information proves," said Ovid, "that they only begin to drink to deaden their feelings."

A few paragraphs back, I mentioned that most people do nothing under the influence of liquor that they ordinarily wouldn't do without it. I'd like to explore this point further. There is, as we have seen, a certain degree of canceling out of effects between sexual and alcoholic indulgence. Most of us can recall, if we think about it, how satisfactory sexual intercourse and a satisfying drinking experience (not intoxication) both tend to allay restlessness and irritability and help produce a condition of contentment and self-satisfaction. If we are looking for temporary release from the grip of inner threats and outer pressures, we ought to be able to have sex without alcohol, or vice versa. My experience with alcoholics bears this out.

Male alcoholics, especially when they are drinking, are not much interested in sexual activity; nor do alcoholic women express their sexuality more freely while under intoxication. You must read those two statements carefully, because the conclusion-jumpers may end up with the wrong answers. I did not say alcoholics avoided sex. I said *intoxication does not promote unusual interest in sexual activity among alcoholics I have studied.* Let me give you a brief case history to illustrate this point. An alcoholic husband was the next-door neighbor of an alcoholic wife. During sober moments both had recognized their strong sexual attraction for each other. But faced with problems enough already, both sensibly set aside their lustful longings. Quite by accident, however, they began to drink together one evening and, under the spell of liquor, decided to throw caution aside and give vent to their desire. Driving off in a car with an abundant supply of liquor, they headed for the anonymity of a motel.

Once inside their room, each continued to drink more and more until their real reason for being there seemed unimportant. When, the next morning, the abandoned spouses found their mates nude in the motel bed, they were understandably convinced that a sexual orgy had transpired. But in fact, as was revealed in later psychiatric treatment, the alcohol had taken care of whatever they sought, and sex in no way had been a participant in their drunken adventure.

There is that wide chasm between the social and the problem drinker, however, and you will recall that the latter seeks to fill his insatiable need with alcohol. Not uncommonly, nor surprisingly, "playing at sex" will often be used as an attempt to fill the very same need when alcohol does not suffice. Therefore, an unhealthy, unwise use of alcohol can become the symptom of choice for an emotionally disturbed individual just as unhealthy promiscuity can become the mark of madness for another. Craving for one kind of indulgence lessens the craving for the other. Thus, those who would preach total abstinence from alcohol, voluntary or enforced, in order to promote sexual morality may unwittingly be working for the other side.

You may say these are pathological cases — neurotics and the mentally ill — who give an unrealistic, far-fetched picture when compared to the so-called normal drinker. Unfortunately, we must learn and deduce from the extremes. The extreme is the only one who boils over into undisguisable illness and comes to light so that we may investigate him. He comforts us by the ready recognition of his overt problems, since he permits us nagging escape from our own covert ones.

Now, is the idea of liquor as an ego-builder so silly
and unfamiliar? No, it is not. And how about satisfactory sexual activity — doesn't that bolster your ego, too?
Yes, it does. Moreover, it is true that liquor stimulates
sexual desire — but only superficially. Liquor reduces
self-consciousness; it paves the way. It removes timidity
and lets out the proposition. It unabashes action,
drowns the conscience, and murders fastidiousness
(many a quiet, continuous sexual liaison has required
constant alcohol-priming). Coarseness and crudeness
are made invisible by liquor; enough of it will enable
a street-walker to become a Mona Lisa.

All these are superficial deceptions. Didn't the urge
for sexual activity really nudge us first — and liquor
follow along afterward to prepare and smooth the way?
And haven't liquor and sex each by their anesthetic
qualities helped to deaden temporarily the monotony
of some dull everydays? Haven't they both lulled you
into a deep, delicious sleep? And while you were in
their grip, and after pleasant experiences with both,
have you not felt exalted in your sense of personal importance? And have you not, concurrently, felt a
strange sadness at the ending of a delightful drinking
or sexual experience? Alcohol and sex have the same
wonderful power to lift life to a different perspective.
Both promote repose and relaxation from curriculum
and obligation. Both can provide a momentary sense of
the creative power waiting to be unleashed within us
all. Then, like the unused cells of procreative life that
daily die within us, this powerful lion, with reality

awakened, rolls back upon its meek side and slumbers on.

The neurotic, however, selects one or the other and forces it to an unhappy, funless extreme; he will not likely use both. The true alcohol addict, as the true addict of other narcotics, is not much concerned with sex. His cravings lie in other fields. Conversely, the true satyr, the sex hound, will countenance no dulling of his senses by drugs. Indeed, one shattering, insulting blow to his ego by alcoholic impotency is enough to put him on the wagon for life!

Like its coconspirator liquor, sex is often misunderstood. Psychiatry has been crucified by its focus on sex (especially upon infantile sexuality), and many people have seriously wondered if psychiatrists are nothing but sublimated satyrs. I suppose these same people who cannot tolerate any complexity in their inner experience would also say that surgeons are sublimated sadists, or that firemen are frustrated bedwetters!

The truth is that psychiatrists are professionally interested in sex because it is the thermometer of the personality. Just as the fever signals an infection, a disturbance in sexual activity may signal a personality problem. Not every temperature change means trouble, of course, and not every sexual upset means a problem. The patterning and persistence of the "fever," or sexual difficulty, determine whether the disturbance is real or not. Then there is that old chestnut about infantile sexuality. Here we have a dramatic example of the fundamental failure in communication about sex. When a baby boy of six months fondles his penis and achieves erection, he is enjoying a sexual experience! To stop him or make him feel guilty is not only wasteful but cruel. He is simply enjoying a pleasant sexual sensation (and he isn't thinking of bouncing into other babies' beds), and he probably will have thousands more — direct and symbolic — as he races through life.

Now, those highway robbers of pleasure will undoubtedly tell you to force the child to cease and desist, because he may like it too much and grow up to be a sex hound. Don't you believe it. These wailing warners of doom are only afraid of what might happen to themselves if they were ever sexually stimulated; once let go, they might not want to stop. But the baby does not have that problem. Give him some liquid refreshment and, like the adult with liquor, thoughts of sex will quickly fly away.

No, if sex were merely the insertion of the male organ into that of the female, there would be nothing to it; sex would be like brushing the teeth, getting into a car, or responding to calls of nature. Other bits of nature might resent it, too. The honey bee buzzing from flower to flower, spreading pollen upon the pistil, is happily engaged in sexual activity. The dog who responds to a signal he cannot understand, but must obey, is responding to a need to perpetuate his species. But a man blunts his instincts to make himself a responsible social being; he changes his sexual activity to more than a reflex. Indeed, *healthy sexual activity and adjustment mark the cornerstone of his personal achievement.* Oh, true, like the people who eat and do not dine he may respond instinctively, but he has not had a sexual experience. He has had intercourse, he has relieved himself, he has engaged in intravaginal masturbation — and it really does not matter with whom or for what. He does not relish the anticipation, nor recognize how his knowledge of and feelings for the individual with whom he will share the act may enhance its beauty and meaning. And when he considers the act complete he does not linger to build memories that will keep him emotionally warm. It is finished; let us go (like the American tourist who double parks outside the Louvre so he can run in and see the *Mona Lisa*). Lingering increases memories. With memories firm and related, satisfactions are deep and longer lasting.

Indeed, one reason for the overconcern in Western societies with health and safety is this same lack of lingering, the substitution of rush. Without firm foundations for deeper satisfactions, we discard things in rapid obsolescence. We scan and glance; we do not read. Since people respond to life in patterns, we now hurriedly skim our relationships; we gulp our sex and leave our mates to wonder who was there, feeling used rather than loved.

A sexual experience, on the other hand, can be a thing of beauty and fulfillment; it means more than just sexual intercourse. Unfortunately, Western societies — and Americans in particular — have always behaved as though that were all there was to it. No wonder people are so disappointed that they charge into psychiatric offices in droves. Think back to the tenderness of your desire, not to the avarice of your release. As in the drinking experience described earlier, you are sharing and communicating a fragment of creative human experience, never to be shared in exactly that same way again. Only at that moment can the two of you create forever and for the moment that flow of beauty and joy. As the wine is carefully cradled from vine to bottle to you, so should sexual activity in love be nurtured. Once you give of yourself, and receive unto yourself, in a sexual union with love, then you will soar above the rigors of the race and get some living out of life — all pleasure-killers and pygmies of prehistoric thinking to the contrary.

Liquor can do the same. But my point is, heavy doses of both at the same time are not recommended. If those stories you hear about people who start out innocently and drink themselves into strange arms happened as frequently as some suppose, and in direct proportion to the amount of liquor consumed, the human race would embody millions of sexually exhausted wrecks.

In any discussion of sex, sooner or later we must consider its biological result. In other words, what, if any, effect does alcohol have upon our progeny? I have been told that some geneticists imply that being brought up in an alcohol-prone society improves the strain. I do not know any basis for such a conclusion. What I would prefer to believe is that all those people who have not the capacity to let themselves go, or who are not emotionally mature enough to throw themselves completely into a sexual relation, will one day try a small amount of liquor and lose some of those inhibitions! In many marital sexual experiences, the woman, through frigidity, has narcotized herself against the onslaught of her husband, while the man expels his tension to a stranger. It is done; it has little meaning for either. And it will produce meaningless memories. If conception ensues, the pregnancy has not the same beauty and meaning as that born out of a mutual embrace. Indeed, the child may not be the same, for subtle maternal and paternal feelings can later tell him so much about his parents and how they really feel about him. On the other hand, should a moment of sexual beauty feed a marriage and conception ensue, both partners can reminisce happily about their mischievous pleasure, and the newborn child will be viewed with a warmer, more favoring eye. We all know how important being made to feel wanted and warm in one's home is to a child's emotional security.

For the moment let us say that the partners of a marital union wish to free themselves of their inhibitions and restrictions of the past. They want to experience and to give together, and so they share a small amount of liquor together — not to get drunk, but to relax. And in the coverlets of their private domain, they reach that mountain peak from which they, and they alone, view the valleys of the world for a brief moment. Will not that woman and mother-to-be smile inwardly at the memories of that precious moment whenever she feels the life stirring inside? And won't that woman and her man look with an added glow upon their howling image as they recall the spark of joy that led it there?

Contrast that experience with the child born to parents who have by their inhibitions psychologically anesthetized themselves to the pleasures of sexual activity, and who feel and behave as though they have been put to the stud. With no beautiful or pleasurable memories to fortify herself, the mother is "snowed" with anesthesia and thereafter presented with a strange, whelping baby. Small wonder that the feelings which greet the new citizen of such a household are not all joy and welcome. There are so many shackles that wear us to the ground. Why not try a little lightening of the load with liquor?

On the other hand, we find people pointing to the children of severely alcoholic parents and saying, "My, how their lives have been ruined." I cannot disagree with this entirely, but I am uncertain whether it is true in any *biological* sense. For example, if a child develops malnutrition because of the neglect or poverty of his parents, this is not biological; it is environmental. We find some children raised in miserable squalor and neglect whose physical health is beyond repair. Yet, I would venture to guess that the physical destruction of children from parental neglect due to alcoholism is no different from the neglect derived from other causes. It is not the alcohol, nor their heredity, that hurts these children. It is the fact that they do not receive proper nourishment, proper hygiene or proper attention.

In one study I know of, an alcoholic woman perpetuated a common law marriage with another alcoholic twenty years her senior. The union produced three offspring. This loosely knit family of five lived in utter squalor and poverty in an abandoned shack at the edge of town. Although the father disappeared for prolonged periods while the mother foraged for food and liquor, their illegitimate children were provided with the essential nutrients for their bodies, as well as for their emotions. The mother, you see, had determined that the love she had not known with her own mother would somehow be provided for her children. Drunk or sober, ill or well, depressed or gay, she always made certain she was at home to care for her kids and lavish much affection upon them. As a result, when this family was studied extensively later on, the children were adjudged in good health physically and showed evidence of every reasonable emotional growth and development.

Contrast this now with another alcoholic family in which both parents came from the "right" families. The father with his inherited wealth had attended some of the better private schools in the Northeast, had gone into the family business, and was an active participant in the necessary community activities. His wife was a lovely lady of a proper family, raised by a cold, calculating mother. Both husband and wife had learned from their first drinking experience that liquor was the necessity of life, and when the cold awakening came that neither cared for the other, liquor became their loyal ally. During their subsequent pursuits of oblivion, their three children were left to fend for themselves. Because no one who suspected the truth would admit it, no one stepped in. Meanwhile, the parents ended up in strange places at strange times, sometimes disappearing for days. When these children were examined, their nutritional state was found to be marginal and they were considered severely disturbed emotionally and in need of psychiatric help.

The truth of the matter, as I have seen it, is this: the cared-for children of severely alcoholic parents are generally in the same range of normal physical health as children of nonalcoholic parents. Emotionally, of course, we have a horse of another color. But may I remind you that we are discussing, for a change, the positive aspect of liquor — *and alcoholism is not on the positive side of anything*. Unfortunately, the emphasis in society has always been on the abnormal reaction, rather than the healthy one. It is as though, because we know that cancer is manifested by an abnormal, heightened growth of cells, we were to advocate the elimination of *all* growth.

On the other side of the coin (the positive one, that is), the proponents point out that liquor, taken daily by the normal individual in moderate, "nontoxic" doses, is not injurious to him or his offspring. The tissues of reproduction are hardy; indeed they are understandably the toughest of all human tissue. Of course, enough concentration of alcohol could kill these bits of eternity, but the nature of the beast is such that the parents would long since be dead before such a concentration could be reached. It would take far less alcohol to kill the adult than to destroy his reproductive cells.

As for the role of genetics in liquor use, there is not much information around. Some say it was the aristocratic families who had the time and money to drink often and well, and therefore they and their progeny became the ego-ideal of human breeding. In other societies — and I suspect in America as well — the rider on the upper rung of the social ladder was the one who set the standard for those qualities worth breeding in humans.

There have been, of course, laboratory experiments to prove, supposedly, how liquor improves races. In one major fifteen-year study by C. R. Stockard, guinea pigs — five thousand of them — were used, presumably because this lowly little mammal has his procreative cells placed and protected in his body much the same as humans. Because the pig's placental and uterine attachments are closely similar to the human setup, it was assumed that substances in the pig's blood reached the reproductive cells by routes similar to those in man. (Both guinea pigs and man, by the way, respond to heavy doses of liquor in the same way: they weave, stagger, fall, and finally pass out.) In the preliminary study, the quality and heredity of the animals were stressed; only pedigreed pigs were used, and all were pretested for fertility. The animals were segregated into treated and untreated (alcoholized or nonalcoholized) groups, but the selection was such that the groups were of equivalent blood lines of stock.

To avoid the possibility of digestive disturbance, alcohol was administered daily by inhalation. Intoxicated the pigs were made and intoxicated they remained. Some managed six years of this existence — which is a healthy old age for any pig, drunk or sober. No evidence was produced to show that alcohol shortened life, nor was there any evidence that constant exposure to alcohol injured health or damaged specific organs. This should not surprise the persistent and diligent reader. What may surprise you, though, concerns the descendents of these two groups.

Normal guinea pigs have a high mortality rate. Most loss occurs during pregnancy or shortly after, yielding a fifty-fifty prenatal/postnatal ratio of deaths. In the nonalcoholized pigs, this death ratio was maintained. The progeny of the alcoholic pigs, however, knocked the ratio far out of kilter: more pigs, twice as many, were lost during pregnancy than after. The conclusion drawn by the researchers: among the "weaker" embryos, alcohol acted to eliminate far more than would have died normally (presumably leaving strong, heathy survivors). Although successive pig generations from alcohol-laden families expired in greater number than those from the unintoxicated, this was attributed to the theory that the strongest survive, the weakest perish. In time, the offspring of the alcoholized group began producing "strong, vigorous" pigs, thus demonstrating that alcohol had eliminated the weak from the stock but had not lowered the quality of the strong.

This may be persistent research, but it is not good genetics.

Another racial-stock improver, Walton Smith, went farther in his research. He reviewed studies of offspring of severely alcoholic parents, compared them with children of nonalcoholic parents, and found that although the death rate was higher — due primarily to accidents and neglect — height, weight and general health among the surviving alcoholic children were equal to or better than those of the sober group.

The above may be an interesting observation, but again it is not good genetics (and it has some unhealthy racist implications). Let's be reasonable: "pigs is pigs" and people are people. So often we find the biased researcher proving his point about human behavior through the study of animals. Animal study is important, as in any science, and sophisticated animal researchers do not need my defense. But what occurs, unhappily, is that the unsophisticated, in their fervor to prove a point, frantically (and cleverly) extrapolate animal findings upon humans and assume they are comparing the same thing.

Not so.

On the subject of proper experiment, take, for example, the topic of alcohol and longevity. You have heard perhaps the statement that if you drink you will die. Life insurance company statistics have been quoted to show that the use of alcohol actually shortens life. But are the conclusion-jumpers aware of how alcohol-longevity statistics are collected by insurance companies? When a man applies for insurance coverage, he is invariably questioned about his drinking behavior. Now, granting that every applicant tells the truth when he applies, the picture of his alcoholic habits can be only of that time and the immediate past. Nothing takes into account the possibility that drinking habits change *in both directions*: some people become heavier drinkers, others drink less. Thus, a wealth of experience is lost by this mixture in the category "drinkers" of unknown proportions of people who have been or will be abstainers, moderate drinkers and excessive drinkers for the major part of their lives. Once the individual applicant has been signed up, the only knowledge the insurance company will ever have about him — beyond the original information on his application — will be the fact that he continues to exist (as evidenced by his premium payments) or that he has passed away (as evidenced by the final claim).

Moreover, most people feel that insurance companies discriminate against persons using alcohol, and so there is a strong incentive to understate the amount of liquor consumed for fear the company will respond by not issuing the policy or by increasing the premium rate. One need not be a sophisticated experimenter to see how erroneous conclusions can be reached in either direction by such approaches. You may get any result that your prejudice desires by statistical manipulation. Yet this is the same level of learning employed in the study of alcohol and its effect upon us. All that we can really say with our present knowledge is that regular liquor use in moderate, nontoxic amounts does not directly shorten or prolong life.

I have heard recently that one insurance company advertises that it will offer a lower insurance rate to the nondrinker. Perhaps this company has recognized the nature of man's self-interpretation, judgment and honesty when it comes to money matters and has concluded that if people are going to be dishonest anyway, why not use it as an advertising gimmick?

In closing a chapter on liquor and sex, a question comes to mind about alcohol use and the strength of a nation and its people. A few pages ago, I pointed out that robes of deity were necessary to give another being your own value system. Here, too, the wisdom of a god is required. The strength of nations and people requires much definition. What are the criteria to be used, and how measured? Shall they be judged by their wealth, creativity, productivity, laws, culture, conquests, religions, family size, height, weight, intelligence? And can you filter out one substance, one cause, as the major contributory factor to the strength of a nation and its people? I can't, and yet I have seen it written that the strongest nations have a far higher alcohol history than the weak, and that the strongest nations have a far lower alcohol history than the weak. Both statements are probably correct — depending on

your definition of strong or weak and high or low —
since only the Eskimo has no ready source for alcohol
production.

I do not wish to let you think that liquor, and
liquor alone, is the prescription for happiness. I can
only say that if you choose to drink, and you learn
to drink sensibly as well, then you have a means of
reaching at times those you want to reach. The lone-
liness will be a little less; the discomforts will diminish.
Those little bubbles of expression will come forth —
and for those moments, and I sincerely hope many
others as well, you will be free of fear.

5

Thy Children Are Like an Arrow

PEOPLE have always assumed that drinking during adolescence, sometimes to excess, inevitably leads to alcoholism. They make this assumption because in the histories of alcoholic patients we find a high percentage of problem drinkers in the family. And more studies in abundance are continually being made to link up the drinking practices of teenagers with the destructive behavior of the problem drinker. Indeed, whenever the scaremongers want to win adherents to their cause against the evils of liquor, teenage drinking becomes their certain target. To most parents, who are afraid of their offspring anyway, the mere thought that drinking during "terrible teenage" might unleash forces leading to drunkenness and alcoholism is enough to ring the alarm bell.

Now let us straighten out one thing fast: *teenage drinking is not alcoholism*. Teenage drinking is what it says it is: the use of alcohol by boys and girls in their teens. We are not talking here about unhealthy social, physical or economic adjustment with alcohol. It's important to make this distinction between alcoholism and teenage drinking because the former is a problem we can all agree needs helping. But when the talk turns to teenage drinking, I can't agree there's a problem at all. And if there's no problem, what are we getting excited about?

Back in the forties, some scientific busybody found that 40 per cent of high school boys and 20 per cent of the girls had consumed some alcohol during the year studied. In a separate study during this same period about 35 per cent of the children confessed to sometimes drinking beer, wine or spirits. By the early fifties, 45 per cent of the kids were owning up to a some-time drink. The mid-fifties brought admissions of drinking up to 86 per cent, two thirds of the teenagers considering themselves social users. And more recently, a New York State legislative committee reported that 59 per cent of a large group of children in the fourteen to eighteen age group were using alcoholic beverages.

"See, children drink early and often," cry the frightened. Not so. They just own up more readily. There is no need to deceive themselves, as their parents do, about the obvious. It's about time we faced this fact: in spite of our laws, our concerns, our warnings, teenagers drink more often than not. This is not solely an American observation, but it applies in other Western societies as well.

Recently, a clergyman in New Zealand stirred up a

controversy with this statement: "Liquor [and] sex . . . if used properly can lead to a fuller life." As a participant in a conference on the problems of youth, he mainly criticized the church for not always giving young people relevant and effective moral guidance. Many of the youths expressed confusion over various laws concerning the acceptable age for voting, marrying, drinking and driving. For example, youths in New Zealand vote and drink liquor legally at twenty-one, serve in the armed forces at twenty, pay taxes in their teens, are licensed to drive a car at fourteen, and are permitted to marry at sixteen.

Recently they asked that the licensing hours be altered to embrace wider drinking hours so as to eliminate the "false emphasis on drinking and allow it to assume its rightful place in society." It appears that children can be more aware of the ways of the world than the so-called wise adults!

Now what else do these children tell us about liquor and themselves? It will come as no surprise, but beer is the most widely used beverage among teenage drinkers; wine is next, followed by spirits. Obviously, as their ages increase, so do frequency and content. And recently, a Scandanavian researcher released his finding that teenage drinking behavior is equivalent in Denmark, Norway, Finland and Sweden, in spite of differences among their laws and social attitudes toward drink.

Now here is something that ought to worry (or reassure) you: all studies agree there is a very strong tie-in with respect to parental attitudes and drinking practices among our children. Abstainers raise abstainers; drinkers raise drinkers. Occasional users have offspring who drink occasionally; regular users have offspring who drink regularly. My guess is that this study indicates, if nothing else, why we are so afraid of our offspring: they mirror us. What a horrible, frightening thought!

The concern we have about our juveniles is not new. According to the inscription of an Assyrian tablet of the year 2800 B.C., an ancient lamented modernly: "Our earth is degenerate in these latter days. There are signs that the world is speedily coming to an end. Bribery and corruption are common. Children no longer obey their parents."

Socrates, some 2350 years ago, further commented that children pursued luxury and showed disrespect for their elders, loving "chatter in place of exercise. Children are now tyrants, not the servants of their households." Sadly, Socrates went on that the youth of his day "no longer rise when elders enter the room. They contradict their parents, chatter before company, gobble up dainties at the table, cross their legs, and tyrannize over their teachers." Times do not change! I am only sorry that I have been unable to find reference to a concern by our ancestors for children drinking, especially when driving their chariots so as to endanger.

We ought to ask ourselves (remember Socrates — the unexamined life is not worth the living), what does it mean to a teenager to drink? As parents, we know we cannot understand adolescents. But we can listen. In case you don't remember, adolescence is complex and confusing. A teenager is neither fish nor fowl, child nor grown-up. It is a unique period of insecurity and strain, both from the adolescent's view and from the perception of those about him. The toughness of the age is caused, on the one hand, by the need to become independent of family while becoming socially responsible to others, and, on the other hand, by that remaining tug toward being, as before, protected and dependent. Sociologists label the sudden and abrupt press for independence a rite of passage in our society. Other, so-called less sophisticated societies have formal, ceremonial rites of passage whereby visible signposts say to adolescent and adult alike: He is free, so let him be.

More sophisticated societies have smudged guidelines. You cannot tell the men from the women, the parents from the kids, without a scorecard. But children, in their infinite wisdom, make their own scorecards and signposts — and liquor use is a quite visible sign (or passage rite) which an adolescent can take for himself as a meaningful demonstration of independence and near-adult status. Western societies have inconsistently based rites of passage from child- to adulthood on chronological age: drinking at one age, the permission to drive at another, the compulsion to serve in the military at another, and so on. Teenagers, on the other hand, view graduating from high school, taking on a full-time job, getting married and entering the armed forces as rites into adulthood. In contrast to legal rites of passage, adolescents measure adulthood by achievement. Since society sets legal recognition of adulthood at differing ages, the youth reaching for guidelines will snatch at any easily available, but tabooed, one. Liquor drinking is such a guideline. Drinking, because it is forbidden, becomes dramatic and romantic; it allows partaking of an adult-like role.

Rites of passage are important and should not be sloughed off. In primitive societies the rite of passage permits the youth, now adjudged a man, to assume new responsibilities, share different pleasures and be independent in some actions. The ancient Jewish rite of passage at age thirteen, the bar mitzvah, is a good example of a rite of passage from youth to manhood. Incidentally, liquor is an important guest at the celebration of this momentous event. The phrase constantly repeated to the bar mitzvah-ed teenager is, "Today, you are a man!" There is no if, and or but about it; in a single moment the boy is declared a man. From then on, he can partake in all religious ceremonies of Judaism, and these all include liquor, directly or indirectly, as an offering. There is no question in my mind, however, that the acculturation of Jewish adolescents to the greater society around them, to the constant needs of their mothers to keep them dependent, and to the dilution of the desirability of orthodoxy, all have led to a diminished significance of the bar mitzvah as a rite of passage.

We adults quickly and conveniently forget that teen-age drinking studies show consistently that drinking indicates a distinct relation to the passage from youth into young adult roles. Laws which prevent our young people from making the adult decision about drinking before age twenty-one say, in essence, that those among us who may marry, work and fight in wars are not old enough to decide whether or not they should drink.

Remember, too, that beyond independence the adolescent has to learn how to be socially responsible to others. Here liquor is beneficial once again. Most findings show that teenage drinking occurs in groups, at parties. This is important. Children of Western societies are dedicated to being somewhat irresponsible, to "having a good time." There is strong emphasis on social activity with the opposite sex, a major interest in athletics and physical activities, and, above all, a worship of physical attractiveness. Liquor fits naturally into this youth culture orientation of having a good time, of being a popular member of the crowd. In other words, our teenagers create, knowingly or unknowingly, their own set of drinking behaviors.

What are these behaviors? First of all, teenagers are moderate users of alcohol beverages: they mainly like beer. As they advance in age, of course, they drink more often and in greater quantity; but most important, they drink in groups and as part of their social pattern, which is a healthy set of behaviors.

"Is that all there is to teenage drinking?" the disbelievers say. Although we hear of many isolated instances of teenage drinking in association with crimes, accidents and deviant social behavior — thus causing the latent anxieties we parents have about our adolescents as they blossom into bloom — the fact of the matter is this: *there is no known correlation between drinking and teenage troubles.* Delinquents drink and so do nondelinquents.

If we are right about this (and we are), then what exactly is the problem about teenage drinking? First, let us quickly review: teenage drinking is common and is not alcoholism; liquor for the teenager reflects an identification with adults; it attempts to ease the adolescent's passage to adulthood; and it fits into the youth culture orientation of fun, irresponsibility and sociability. We have further said that "normal" teenage drinking is the rule, unhealthy drinking the exception. So where is the problem? It rests squarely with the adults.

On the surface, adults disapprove of teenage drinking, even though they themselves may drink heavily and permit alcohol to the teenager in the home. No, we express our disapproval in our legislative and voting behavior, by prohibiting the sale or use of liquor out of the house. Indecisive, inconsistent and ambivalent toward adolescent drinking, we parents epitomize our confused concern with our young — and these same inconsistencies reflect themselves on our children. We tell them it's all right to drink at home, but it's taboo away; yet we parents do more drinking away than at home!

We forget that liquor provides a means of socializing and of identifying the teenager's entrance to adulthood. Instead, we parents prefer to maintain our favorite image of them: as bobby-soxers devouring ice cream sodas.

These conflicting and strange attitudes toward liquor really are the problem-makers. Here's another example of what happens when adults issue orders contrary to the way they usually want to behave: a federal prohibition act was passed in the United States even after — as early as 1871 — all the New England states had prohibition laws, and all but one had been repealed. There should be no need to explain what happened to the prohibition law in the United States, as well as in every country that ever tried to row against the natural tide (India, as an example, has just failed with prohibition). Adults devise methods to rebel against laws contrary to their wishes; therefore, why shouldn't adolescents!

Quick, easy answers are always forthcoming. Put labels on liquor bottles, some argue, stating: "May cause intoxication, neuralgia, paralysis, neuritis, mental derangement, kidney and liver damage," and so forth. Others suggest issuing personal liquor licenses for the right to buy liquor, or raising the drinking age. Recently, I was asked to testify in the battle of two states wishing a third to raise the drinking age to twenty-one. The reason: teenagers from Connecticut and New Jersey, where the legal drinking age is twenty-one, were driving to New York, where the legal age is eighteen, and were getting into car accidents on the way home. My suggestion: instead of pummeling the third state to raise the age limit, why not have the others lower theirs! That way the teenagers wouldn't have to drive so far to get their drinks and therefore would avoid most of the accidents. Result: I was not asked to testify.

We can see how easy it is to delude ourselves about liquor, teenagers and laws to regulate drinking behavior. While New Jersey, allied with Connecticut, has been waging war against the lenient drinking laws of New York, its own backyard has been "polluted." In Mendham, New Jersey, the police had to lead a charge against thirty to forty boys and girls, some as young as fourteen, who were attending a teenage beer party. The chief of police himself led the raid. Many slipped away through doors and windows when the police appeared, and only a few were apprehended. The older teenagers were charged with contributing to the delinquency of minors, the younger with possessing and consuming alcoholic beverages. This episode may seem slightly humorous at first, but I don't happen to think it's funny at all. These adolescents were drinking beer — a substance as freely available as soft drinks — in a group setting, and yet they were treated as though they were narcotic smugglers! Can you imagine the unhealthy attitude toward liquor these children will develop?

There is further evidence that parents and legislators are swimming against the positive tide. Aware how accurately novelists reflect their times, one study by H. W. Pfautz notes that in recent years fifty per cent more references have been made to alcohol in modern fiction than in novels written at the beginning of the century. Drinking, formerly a male pastime, is now carried on freely by groups of men and women in literature, and liquor is more positively portrayed as a helpful, rather than a harmful, substance.

Can you see the circle that has been accomplished? You cannot really talk about teenage drinking without also talking about the meaning of alcohol in an entire society. In our Western society, alcohol is acceptable among adults, with thirteen out of fourteen users showing no behavior disorders. Since the problem is not as universal as intimated, is it not absurd (and even harmful) for us to build a case against teenage drinking as another cause for alarm? Rather, we ought to see teenage drinking for what it is — a sort of minor league try-out for the adult big leagues.

Bearing all these points in mind, I would like now to make a strong suggestion. *Let's get rid of the age limit for drinking.* It is unfair, inconsistent and foolish. Any parent, any adult, can buy liquor and supply it to a child. But once we are out in public, our attitudes mysteriously change: no alcohol for the kids outside the home, and punish anyone who provides it to them. Some will argue, of course, that certain activities should be completely private and unshared, that others should be shared only in small groups, such as families, while still others can be enjoyed most anywhere. If adults drank at home exclusively, I would agree.

But since we don't legislate restrictions about other readily available foodstuffs, why do we pick on liquor? Why don't we pass laws specifying when children can eat steak, or choke on spinach, or drink coffee? Liquor isn't a foodstuff but a drug, some will argue. Are we suggesting that drugs be easily provided? I respond: *drugs are limited to adults, limit them to teenagers.* Our sociologists have shown us that the Italian and Orthodox Jewish children have alcohol available to them from early in life on, yet liquor problems are few and far between. We Westerners, on the other hand, give our children a healthy drinking experience at home, while at the same time creating conditions outside which make drinking for teenagers a furtive, shameful, guilt-ridden — and law-breaking — affair.

I propose that we rid ourselves of this furtiveness, this negative attitude about teenagers drinking outside of the home. True, we may be depriving them of some of the fun of sneaking it, but at least they will have less opportunity to use it unhealthfully. Also, in addition to the relaxation and removal of drinking-age limits, why couldn't high school teachers, college professors and deans throw an occasional sherry party, instead of serving the traditional tea? These are the models teenagers use for identification (not always the best, but models nonetheless); if students could see these important people, who are daily influencing their emotional growth, treat alcohol as just another beverage, then they would soon feel the same way about it.

Recently, in answer to a suggestion similar to the above, there came a vehement response to the effect that this method would corrupt the youth of our country. I say, corruption among men exists and will increase so long as we continue to set up more and more unrealistic rules — rules which are easily broken. Liquor is easy to acquire; it is an accepted part of Western society. The sooner we accept these two facts, the sooner we will have less difficulty with alcohol.

I do not now — and never will — advocate that everyone should drink. This is a decision each person must make for himself. Most troublesome, though, is the attitude that if liquor is not for me, then you can't have it either; or that it's fine for me, but it's harmful for my children. When alcohol is given such special significance, a child in revolt finds it an easy and natural substance to turn to when the time comes to defy his family and society. We should realize that if we drink, our offspring will drink. If we do not drink, they ought to know why and then make up their own minds (they will anyway!). But first, parents should establish the amount of liquor they are willing for their children to drink. Just as the child does not receive the same portion of food as the adult, so should he not receive the same portion of liquor.

Also, parents must decide when their children are mature enough to make their own decision as to drinking. This is a common concern of parents, for decision making means being permitted to make mistakes. If children are so protected and so dependent that they never have the chance to make mistakes, then they will never be able to make decisions. Part of the problem is that we are so overconcerned about our children, so busy sticking our noses into their lives, that we do not permit them to make mistakes; and without some experience in decision making, they will never develop any confidence in their ability to take decisive action. If a three-year-old child wishes to cross a busy turnpike alone, the parent will hopefully be realistic enough to say no. But if the same child should want a taste of liquor, the worst that can happen to him is some slight stomach upset; more probably, he will dislike the taste intensely and hate the stuff forever. It may even help him decide in the future whether or not he wants to bother with liquor at all.

But what happens, say those same frightened voices, if the child enjoys his taste of liquor and gets a "glow"? There is nothing wrong with the glow and joy of liquor, nor does it portend disaster. Most of us have had "glows" from drinking, and yet most of us use alcohol in a very healthy way. But then, some people oppose *any* sort of pleasurable stimulation, because "it might form some sort of habit." The one habit I worry about, where teenagers are concerned, is the parental habit of killing pleasure for teenagers. So many adults have had such miserable, unhappy, confused adolescent periods that they are unconsciously determined that their children must pass through the same kind of hell. They limit their teenagers' pleasure by all manner of fearful warnings and statistics; they make sure that they get the habit of running in the same old rut, existing without really living; and most important, they make their children forever guilty and fearful of alcohol and sex, or sex and alcohol.

Another point often raised concerns adolescent drinking and juvenile delinquency. Some teenagers who wish to break out, to throw over the traces, manage to retain a measure of control so long as they are without liquor. With liquor, however, might not some of these controls break down so that the teenager will do things he might not have done otherwise? Perhaps — but this is not the whole story.

Children will get into trouble because of drinking and because of a lot of other things, too. It is not that youngsters are going to lose control with liquor and then become delinquents, because delinquents can use alcohol, or situations, or almost anything at all to get into trouble. One form of antidelinquency is group pressure: if you are deviant in behavior, then out of the group you go; but if you behave and commit no major delinquency, no group ostracism. Remember that normal teenage drinking behavior is group-directed. If you create a prohibition and an aversion to drinking outside the home, you alienate the child from group protectiveness.

An excellent example of the effectiveness of group pressure is seen in the kibbutzim (collective farms) of Israel. The major cities of Israel are plagued by delinquency similar to the problems of urban areas everywhere. On the kibbutz, however, delinquency or other unhealthy social behavior is rare; there, you must respect the social codes of the group or out you go.

A brief case history may further illustrate the point. Jimmie was the seventeen-year-old only child of Mormon parents. The prohibitions against drinking were strong, but many of his friends drank. Since he could not permit himself to join in, but with curiosity aroused, he began surreptitiously — and guiltily — buying beer and consuming it secretly with resultant nausea, vomiting and headache.

Later, when Jimmie went east to college, he found that his new friends also liked to drink beer. At first, he found himself drinking too much too fast, and he became ill; his friends made no secret of their disapproval. Subsequent discussion with his guidance counselor, involving some talk about liquor having a positive social value, enabled Jimmie in time to drink with the boys without illness or guilt.

This same group protectiveness helps explain why the Italian or Jewish child can drink early and often without suffering alcoholism, while the French, with the same custom, *do* suffer. The answer is simple: French drinking practices are quite different than that of Italian or Orthodox Jew. Although the French populace drinks freely, there is much conflict, ambivalence and functionalism in their drinking. Many a French farmer must have his brandy first thing in the morning in order to get to work, not as part of a social or religious function. Thus, the French use liquor more in order to function; this has vastly different implications for the child who grows up in such a setting as against the child who is raised to view liquor as just another foodstuff or part of a religious rite.

Yugoslavia is a country that has many juvenile alcohol problems. Rural children from age five and up are suffering the consequence of too much of a good thing. Yugoslavia has great groves of delicious plum trees, and the rural dwellers make home-brew slivovitz (plum brandy). Mothers believe that the exudate of plums increases the quality of the children's blood, protecting them against illness. They ascribe to alcohol a healthy, god-given function with a positive value. The problem is, these Yugoslavian mothers overdo it; they force slivovitz into the mouths of their babes on the old theory that if one drink will make a child one part stronger, ten drinks will make him ten times stronger! The result: a lot of intoxicated children. The blame falls on liquor, but the fault lies solely with the people who use it stupidly.

And so we have learned this much about teenagers and drink: that they do drink, and that they drink as their parents drink — a lot or a little — and that they drink in groups.

But nowhere, in all our studies, is there a shred of evidence that equates teenage drinking and alcoholism. As in all other aspects of the liquor question, they are two entirely different matters. And they always will be.

6

Is It a Crime to Be Ill?

THE Federal Bureau of Investigation, in its Uniform
Crime Reports, reveals that the crime of drunkenness
represents more than forty per cent of all arrests and
leads the nation as the major single crime. Massachusetts, for example, makes more arrests and metes out
more jail sentences for drunkenness than for all other
crimes combined (minor traffic violations excluded).

As you can see, the relation between alcohol use and
criminal behavior is a continuing source of concern.
Often it seems as though, if we could rid society of
alcohol, we could rid the world of crime. And it is certainly true that if we changed the attitude toward alcohol, we could lower our crime statistics substantially,
for the simple reason that whenever society is confronted with some behavior it cannot understand and is
afraid of, it labels it criminal. Thus for the same reason
lepers were once considered criminals to be punished
and ostracized, and mental patients were used as fodder

for fire or languished in poisonous prisons. So too are drunkenness and alcoholism considered crimes. Indeed, most social systems today, as in the United States, report their highest criminal statistics in the area of drunkenness. Since neither the medical profession in particular, nor society in general, seems interested in the problem, it is left to the police to label both intoxication (a metabolic disturbance) and alcoholism (a mental disease) as crimes. And yet, other intoxications and most physical or mental disorders are not now so labeled.

But liquor has strange, interesting effects upon us — not alone from within, but often more disastrously from without. It troubles me that the police are so burdened by the metabolic disturbance of drunkenness. I am certain that they have enough to do without caring for people who find themselves sick from too much liquor. Yet the police, in self-defense (and because they, of course, also reflect the values of society), have their own selective system. In coming to a decision to arrest or not to arrest an individual for public drunkenness, they use some strange criteria. Sad to say, I suspect they use social-class status, what neighborhood the person comes from, in their determination; thus, the fellow who looks dirty, disheveled and down-and-out, and whose address is in the less desirable part of town, gets booked by the police much more rapidly than the drunk who is clean, neat and well-dressed, and whose address is in a more opulent neighborhood. As the late, great Clarence Darrow pointed out, the designation of crime and jail is more readily applied to those of the poorer classes; the same seems to hold true in greater number for the crime of drunkenness.

As we have already seen, the drinking of liquor is a very ancient and usually honorable right of mankind. Can you imagine how our criminal statistics would go up if eating, under certain conditions, were declared a crime? Imagine the police booking people who had had an overdose of fatty foods, thereby putting themselves in danger of coronary disease! Or the poor diabetic who decided he'd have two pieces of candy for the road. And, if we wanted to stretch our analogy, we could arrest people for coughing too often, or for taking too many vitamins or too many tranquilizers. In all seriousness, by falsely labeling intoxication a crime we have placed just such an undue burden on our police departments.

But we are looking at liquor and crime. Let us see how they tie together, if indeed they do. Most views of liquor and crime take the simplest course: if a person has had some alcohol and commits a crime, then alcohol either was the cause of that crime or it released primitive impulses which caused the crime. Now in this vast, complex society of ours simple cause-and-effect answers are attractive, just as quickie cures, facile solutions and glib promotions are attractive to most people. "Use this product, it's the best." "Take this pill, and your marriage will improve." Everyone is plied with simple answers to very complex questions.

I digress this way simply because the idea has been sold to the public that alcohol and crime are inextricably interwoven. In each one of us, alcohol use is a highly complex phenomenon, and not simply the art of taking a drink. The same holds true for committing a crime; few realize that if each criminal act were merely a black-and-white situation, we would have no need for our highly complicated judicial system. Rather, we must first determine what preceded the act of crime, what was the motivation, whether indeed a crime was actually committed, and under what possibly extenuating circumstances.

By the same token, in considering the man who drinks we must bear in mind many details: the type of beverage chosen, the amount and the frequency of drinking, each resulting from an interplay of forces in the emotional makeup of the person; also, what groups he has close ties to, the particular cultures in which he has developed, and the specific circumstances under which the drinking occurs. The contribution of any one of the foregoing will vary from time to time and from drinking episode to drinking episode. For example, a Jew will take wine on Friday with the evening meal; this is *drinking related to cultural development*. The same Jew may work in a store where, on Tuesday night after bowling, the boys have some beer: *drinking related to close group feelings*. When he was a boy, his father forced him to taste scotch whiskey so that now he is revulsed by it. Accidentally, he smells some scotch and feels nauseous: *a personality response*. Or he is drinking in a bar in a strange locale, feeling tense, gulping his drinks and, without realizing it, ordering more than his usual amount: *a situational effect.* These are only a few of the possible psychological, societal, cultural and situational factors that can influence our response to liquor.

Now that you have seen how we look at liquor before and during use, let us examine how we behave after we have had some liquor, for this is important and is one of its delights — and frights. As in the act of drinking liquor, our behavior afterward is also in response to our personality, society, culture and situation. By this I do not mean to minimize the pharmacological action of alcohol itself; but pharmacological response to any drug, we must remember, is extremely sensitive to psychological and social influence. For example, how many times have you thought, "I'll really tie one on tonight!" and from the first sip been high? How many times have you thought, "I can't mix my drinks tonight because I'll get sick" — and then mixed them and been sick? And haven't you heard people say, "I can't drink martinis — they're too strong. But I'll have a Manhattan" (just as strong). Fortunately, or unfortunately, our response to an alcohol beverage and a drinking experience often becomes *what we expect it to be.* Myths and misconceptions, as we have seen, abound around liquor; hence, there are many and varied myths to which we can respond as though they were realities. The main point is this: the pharmacological effects of beverage alcohol cannot be fully understood without a careful examination of psychological and social influences.

Now we know that criminal behavior sometimes

occurs, as do many other behaviors, during or after drinking. How can we measure the relationship? If we were to ignore for a moment the problem of defining "criminality" and "crime," does this relationship indict liquor as a direct or indirect cause of crime? Or does it mean that alcohol releases antisocial impulses which are expressed in criminal acts? The answer is unquestionably NO. Let us face facts:

1. *Many, many more people who drink alcohol do not commit crimes than do.*

2. *Many people commit crimes who have not been near a bottle.*

The point is, you cannot expect a simple answer to a complex question. Forgive me for harping on this fact, but to the audience of this book — those who want to live a lot and who wish to appreciate fully the role of liquor — repetition is required. There is no doubt that alcohol releases a variety of impulses: social, asocial and antisocial. Do not forget, however, that liquor also *inhibits* impulses by way of its narcotizing effects. Nor must we assume that because an impulse is released, the individual will act upon it. On the contrary, he may enjoy these temptingly released impulses by talking or dreaming about them.

I had a patient in treatment some years ago who came to me with the complaint that he was a potential criminal and problem drinker. For the past five years this business executive of a large corporation had a nightly ritual: he would come home to his bachelor quarters, have a light meal, and then begin to drink. As he drank, he began to build up in his mind elaborate, detailed plans of undetectable crimes he would commit. Apparently he felt that being a criminal in his fantasy life, while under the influence of a lot of liquor, was satisfying some inner need. What terrified him, and caused him to come to me for help, was the fact that his heavy drinking was getting out of hand. Lately he needed to drink in order to get going in the morning and last through the day. His efficiency was off, the company was in trouble, and people were openly alluding to his dependence on liquor. My executive friend realized that very soon he must do without his liquor; but aside from his need to stop drinking, his major fear was that if he did stop — and thus frustrate his need to be a criminal in his fantasy life — that he might then begin to commit the very crimes he dreamed of!

Unfortunately, we know precious little more about drinking and crime today than we did thirty or forty years ago. There are obvious reasons for this. Our definitions of "crime" and "drinking" are so poor that we cannot communicate and compare our findings or formulations. We confuse intoxication and alcoholism; we do not differentiate crimes against persons from crimes against places; and, of course, the local and national variations of what is drunkenness, alcoholism, crime or noncrime continue to plague us. The most horrible dilemma is that we relate only one half of crime (*i.e.*, detected crime) with alcohol. May I remind the reader that undetected crime also constitutes criminal behavior (although lately, it seems, we behave as though it were otherwise; if you can get away without being caught, it is not criminal), but in the study of crime we must limit ourselves to detected crime alone. Any self-respecting reader of quality detective stories knows, however, that in a well-organized crime the use of alcohol on the job is strictly taboo.

Recently I heard of a patient who came to an alcoholism clinic for help because liquor was interfering with his criminal activity. The patient was a bookie in the numbers racket. For many years his wife had complained and worried about his drinking; he would return home each night after his day's activities were done and silently consume a fifth of scotch, then pass out. Some nights he would become belligerent and beat up his wife, his children and his furniture. But next morning, our bookmaker would be bright-eyed and conscientious in his illegal activity. His wife begged and pleaded with him to get help for his drinking problem, but he refused, denying he had a problem. This pattern persisted for thirty years.

One day, long after his wife had abandoned hope that he would ever do anything about it, he anxiously presented himself to the clinic. It seems he had begun to drink during the day and the liquor made him forget the numbers on which he was receiving bets (a horrible state of affairs for a bookie!), and now that liquor was in fact preventing his success in his criminal activity, he was begging desperately for help.

A quick look at the variations of alcohol use and

crime illustrates how complex an issue it is. Earlier reference was made to the labeling of "drunkenness," "public intoxication" and sometimes "alcoholism" as crimes, but there are other variations: the socially isolated, unemployed alcoholic (who when sober steals in order to satisfy his desire for alcohol); the alcoholic (who steals while intoxicated); the habitual thief (who drinks every evening but who does not steal every evening); the habitual thief (who drinks *except* when he is committing a crime); the teenager (who occasionally drinks with his buddies, until one night they "borrow" a car for a lark); the man in a drunken rage (who kills his wife); the man who drinks to screw up his courage to commit a crime (and does); or the man who drinks to screw up his courage to commit a crime but, as a result of drinking, does not. And so it goes. Do you see why it is silly to say, unqualifiedly, that drinking causes crime? Alcohol use and criminality is a highly complex problem and it cannot be understood without also understanding many other factors which are operating at the same time.

Perhaps Robert Lindner, who coined the phrase "the romance of alcohol," can shed some light on the subject. He was convinced that people had beliefs, values and very definite attitudes about alcohol: "Much of over-indulgence is engaged upon with the full expectation — and hence the preparation . . . for particular effects: and . . . these effects then come about independently of the exertions of the beverage. . . . Embodied in this romance are some of the following canards: drinking makes for courage ... enhances sexual attractiveness and prowess ... increases skillfulness ... makes one happy. ..." Lindner is astute in his observations.

Is it possible that the difficulties we sometimes get into with liquor are not the fault of liquor but are the result of our myths and fantasies? Instead of blame and shame we ought to ask ourselves some questions: Why — and how — do we transmit these myths? Do we spread these misconceptions about liquor so freely that persons suffering depression, sexual anxiety, or low self-esteem turn to alcohol in the belief that it will help them feel better faster? And do our kids and our criminals slink to these romantic notions because the scare-mongers and killjoys frighten them in this direction? It certainly would be tragic if the pleasure-killers and militant do-gooders were responsible for the problems, rather than the pleasures, of the vine. For these are frightening times. Much goes on all over to terrify us. There are those who would push us back to yesteryear, who would shut out all that is new and threatening; and there are those who feel life has always been fright and threat, and who believe that in recognizing the reality of the potential for danger and pleasure in living, they can enjoy whatever pleasures one may while one can.

This book is solidly in sympathy with the latter. In no area can we stress this more than in the foregoing brief discussion of alcohol and crime. And so one last word: we shall never allot to liquor a rightful, healthy role in society so long as we persist in archaically branding as criminal either intoxication or alcoholism. If we do, we shall only be imprisoned by our own ancient shackles.

7

Oil, Gasoline and Liquor

THE world today speeds along its merry way in a swirl of exhaust fumes. New togetherness is fostered by the sport, compact and foreign car craze in which passengers become prisoners, and automobiles, beyond opening new panoramas of formerly forbidden places, turn into killers. In the first half of the twentieth century, when cars were not especially plentiful, the United States saw more of its people destroyed by autos than it lost through all its wars. This civilian murder, this deflowering of the populace, seemingly has a tawny cohort in liquor; indeed, we see frequent reference to drinking and driving. But let us look at the facts more closely.

Automobiles are essentially a means of changing location. Drinking is a method whereby we mortals brighten up the color of our reality. The two do not need to go together; with heavy drinking they *must* not go together. But then, does normal drinking impair and impede our normal driving skills? Some will contend that once you allow a drop of alcohol to trickle down your gullet, you'd better not get behind the wheel. Yet, the work of Indiana researchers recently indicated that persons who drink small amounts of alcohol may actually be better motorists. With a little liquor flowing in the blood, people had fewer accidents, it was discovered, than teetotalers. In a separate investigation, the British found the same startling result: a driver with a small amount of alcohol in his blood is one third less likely to cause an accident than when he is completely sober.

Lest those who abstain complain that "Drink before you drive!" will soon become a new battle cry for motorists, let me reassure them that people who drink heavily and drive do cause, or are involved in, many accidents. Determined as I am in this book to weigh the evidence in favor of liquor, under no circumstances can I envision the combination of heavy drinking and driving. Unless one feels suicidal or homicidal, to drink much and then drive is as foolhardy a behavior as I know of.

To question *how much* alcohol impairs driving, however, is a trap. For one thing, we have no measure of determining normal driving skills. We can test components of driving behavior — such as reaction time, eyesight, risk taking, judgment, intelligence — but we cannot integrate our findings to say: this (or that) is normal driving behavior. In other words, a person may have rapid reactions, hawk-like vision, first-rate judgment and intelligence and still be a terrible driver. Conversely, deficits in any of these qualities may be compensated for beautifully, much as the blind behave to touch. Therefore, if you cannot set a standard of behavior, you cannot talk about measurable, impaired behavior — even though we all know that liquor in appreciable amounts does decrease competence in driving.

If, as we all know, cars are an effective instrument of killing, and liquor hones the blade of the killer, why can't we do something about it? We cannot, apparently, because our society is not willing to pay the price of absolute safety. The fact is, we accept as tolerable some decrease in driving skills. This answer is important, because it underlies the paradox of the safety-seekers. No one has yet raised a voice in favor of limiting the production of cars, or the building of roads, or the extending of franchises; no one has suggested increased taxation to suppress the sale of automobiles; and no one has had the fervor to harangue the people to get back to walking — that god-given physical right of all — and thus avoid the demon killer. (The late President Kennedy and his brother advocated walking for fitness, not to avoid the use of cars.) Such voices have not been raised because, despite the killing, *cars are personally and economically necessary*. Safety is a watchword only when the pleasurable pursuits of others are in jeopardy, when it acts as a means of securing a cause on which to focus, or when the campaign strikes at an economy touching some of the people but not all.

Furthermore, to aim at drinking and driving is to aim at most everyone. Most of us have had some experience in this area; at one time or another we have all had *some* liquor and then driven without accident. For this reason, as a society we are loath to rise up and strike out against a cause in which we have been partisans. Yet the problem of driving after drinking is a big and important one. Lives are snuffed out and property is destroyed; misery abounds. Although one may argue that society tolerates and invites losses of this type, and though we know they will always exist, still no one can take a popular stand for such destruction. True, no one has unquestionably demonstrated that the drunk driver accounts for significantly more than his share of the loss; indeed, we cannot even filter out liquor as a cause for destruction in driving. Fatigue and quarrels, aggressions and aggravation, frustration and tranquilizers, plus a whole host of recognized and unrecognized factors — all may play the primer to the color of the accident.

In California, for example, a study showed that of 766 vehicles stopped in a traffic check, only one drunken driver was found; and in another study involving 23,000 vehicles, five were found drunk — or slightly more than two hundredths of one per cent! To me, that seems a very low percentage, especially in view of the outpour-

ing of wrath and warning about the excesses of drinking and driving. More important is the finding that
those people arrested for drunken driving tend to drink
large amounts in short intervals, and that many of them
have previous arrest records for other types of criminal
behavior. Could this mean that the person who is directly responsible for raising the specter of liquor as an
accessory in car-killing is already an antisocial individual? If so, this may be a case of the problem few
damning the healthy most.

Healthy drinking, I maintain, is a social event done
in the presence of friends and family; no one should
want to destroy his image before these tribal confed-
erates. Heavy drinking followed by driving is therefore
not likely *unless* one wishes to tell one's loved ones and
society to go to hell. Frankly, I believe the vast majority
of people use less self-destructive and murderous
methods of expressing such ill feelings. Therefore, I am
left with the conviction that drunken driving is simply
another manifestation of antisocial behavior, the problem of a few.

Prohibitionists traditionally have had quick-and-easy
solutions for the drinking-driving problem. According
to them, as with others who have the core answer to
overwhelming complexities, man is weak-willed, unable
to resist temptation and avoid abusing a good thing.
Therefore, we must protect man from himself: remove
from him drink and smoke, fats and sex; give him religion and law, morality and slogans until he is saved

from self. Perhaps, to help solve this problem, we might also introduce one of our modern-day miracle contraptions — a gigantic, well-programmed computer, say, that can control and limit the behavior of cars. By inserting into the car-computer a pre-punched card indicating where we wish to go, the car would proceed via the quickest, safest route, thus eliminating another obstacle to our life while simultaneously removing a further need to use our brains.

Since, I trust, we have shown that the problem of drunken driving may not be the great one we suppose, what tangential common difficulties arise? A woman recently was absolved from a drunken-driving charge when, after she was found intoxicated at the wheel of her parked automobile on the runway at the municipal airport, it was discovered the car was out of gasoline. The charge was changed to "being drunk in a public place." In London, a research group found that exhaust fumes may cause symptoms ascribable to intoxication. Some drivers whom police thought to be drunk were suffering mainly from carbon-monoxide poisoning, which causes similar symptoms. The risk of this occurrence is greater than one supposes; carbon-monoxide traces disappear easily before the blood can be tested, and the air intake of modern autos is conducive to drawing in the air of another vehicle's exhaust. Therefore, that weaving, unstable driver in front of you may not be a drunk, but a gassed chauffeur!

Just as parents worry about cars and liquor, the

children are worried too, but for a different reason. A recent newspaper article described the preoccupation of the youth of Massapequa, Long Island, with their cars; each night they face them toward the road in the hope "something" might happen. Most nights nothing does, and the young people bid each other bored good-nights and return home, hoping the next night might turn something up. The article went on to describe the adult population of the town as viewing this mixture of boredom and anticipation with apprehension. The police in turn reflect the concern of the town with these youth clusters, but have not been able to uncover the reasons for them because group cohesiveness does not permit anyone to tell on his friends. They were interested, however, in talking about why they won't drink when they drive. Since the young adults in this New York community are old enough to own cars, they are old enough to drink. But in most cases, when they want to use their cars, they stay out of the bars; quite sensibly, they fear the possibility of arrest for driving under the influence and subsequent loss of their driving privilege.

Of course, alcohol is indirectly involved in many automobile fatalities — particularly those which have been consciously or unconsciously suicidal in intent. Many patients relate how they have used liquor to aid them in softening a suicidal drive. A colleague of mine recently told of one of his patients whose marriage had been a failure for many years, but he refused to admit it. His wife cuckolded him with frozen contempt and still, although the whole world seemed to know, he preferred his psychological ignorance. The day came, however, when the evidence was so great even he had to admit the obvious: his wife was unfaithful. Now it was out in the open; his pride was hurt; the marriage must go.

But the blind pride that had caused him not to see also convinced him that he could not go on. Suicidal thoughts flooded his brain. Death would have been easy, but he had four sons and shrank from the thought of hurting them by killing himself.

The pain was unbearable, however, and on many an occasion he determined to swerve his car suddenly and end it all. He could not do it. He then decided to drink heavily first, and then accomplish the desired deed. But even then he failed.

I could not help but muse, as my colleague related this story, that if the patient had succeeded it would have been construed as further evidence for alcohol as a cause of death on the highway. In a superficial sense, this is true. But in a deeper sense, liquor would have been the ally of a depressed man bent on suicide.

The tragic death in an automobile accident in Darien, Connecticut, involving a seventeen-year-old girl who had attended a teenage party at which liquor was served, has recently erupted into the newspaper columns. This tragedy, and the retaliatory response of the judge, has evoked considerable argument. I guess we all shook our heads at the report of the accident, at the senseless waste of a young life, but would then have passed it quickly from our minds had not the medical report revealed that the eighteen-year-old operator of the car, a boy, had downed twelve scotches and water at the same party. The reaction of the judge was typical: burn down the town to get rid of the mice.

Every shred of evidence we have to date underlines the truth that drinking done within the confines of the home, with parental approval, is in the direction of healthy social drinking. What was not emphasized in this case was the fact that this boy consumed an amount excessive for anyone. The fault lies not with the substance, but with the amount. And yet, when liquor — the horrible "demon rum" of our heritage — is involved, anything goes. The totalitarian principle of invading and policing the privacy of people's homes is even permitted.

The Darien tragedy is an unhappy response to excess, to the parents' fear of imposing limits, and not the blame of liquor per se. Once again, an axe-wielding reformer, backed by the myths of liquor and an ancient invasion-of-privacy law, can in one tragic moment infuse guilt and shame into the hearts and minds of parents and children alike, thereby setting us backward down the road of liquor ignorance and inexperience.

Perhaps one reason why I have questioned the overemphasis on alcohol and driving is that I have been raised by the slogan, "Speed kills!" Yet a recent study by the United States Bureau of Public Roads, on the relationship between highway accidents and speed, confirms a fact that has long been evident to many motorists: a vehicle driven at forty miles an hour is as dangerous to traffic as one driven at eighty in an area where the average speed of all cars is sixty. In other words, the prime safety factor as it pertains to speed lies in keeping pace with the main flow of traffic. Safe drivers are those who maintain the average speed of traffic moving in the same direction.

Excessive speed, like excessive drinking, is hazardous; but excessively slow speed is equally so. The too-slow driver, like the inexperienced drinker, obstructs the normal, legal flow. He compels risk-taking by those behind him; impatient in their desire to pass, he induces them to weave in and out of traffic lanes. The inexperienced drinker may do the same.

A friend of mine, for example, teased me about writing this book. He said those who may read it will think I am preaching drunkenness and practicing hedonism. This does not trouble me so much. What does trouble me is that those irresponsible persons who cannot — and will not — drink sensibly (I'm not talking now about alcoholics) and who cause much of liquor's poor reputation are probably not the kind, unfortunately, who would buy and read this book in the first place.

In reality, the problem of drinking and driving comes down to the problem of our continuing study of liquor and its social significance. We have always confused social drinking and intoxication, and we will continue to do so. Actually, the two are as far apart as working and slavery, eating and obesity, normal sex and nymphomania. One is a useful, important, desirable function; the other, the extreme of disturbance. Drinking is a healthy endeavor; intoxication is a metabolic disturbance, a state of unhealth. I know of no benefit or social use for intoxication, except perhaps the fact that it provides, for liquor-haters, a focus with which to attack all drinkers and drinking.

If he respects himself, if he pays attention to his response to liquor and its effect upon him, and if he wisely drinks for pleasure and not to prove himself, then the experienced, practical drinker will recognize the unfavorable signals and stop. For there is a measure of control each one of us can exert in our reaction to alcohol; once the drinker has become familiar with his reactions, he need not exaggerate his responses. He knows and can anticipate the effects, and consciously or unconsciously try to compensate for them.

Unfortunately, even the best-controlled among us will get drunk if he drinks too much. But only a fool will attempt to drive a car when he has reached this state, even though some people may in fact drive better under the influence of liquor than the driver who has never let a drop touch his lips. Experienced, healthy drinkers develop safety habits to which they can turn; and there are at least a few foolish things he has trained himself *not* to do. If your wife thinks it might be a good idea if she drove the car home some night, and if, immediately and in silent dignity, you move over, then you belong in the healthy, experienced group. With greater membership in this club, the driving-drinking problem will be appreciably reduced — and one more liquor problem will have a clearer boundary.

8

Why Liquor?

HUMAN beings have been imbibing for countless years. And I think it is safe to predict that so long as the species continues to exist, we will keep on imbibing. With all the warnings, with all the fears, we must wonder why. I suspect a simple response would answer the obvious: humans drink because they like it.

But *do* they like it, except in a limited sense? Certainly as a thirst-quencher it cannot achieve high marks, because it raises thirst. As for taste, the initial experience is not often a great gustatory delight, even when the liquor is sweet. With training, people may change their mind about taste, but this is due more likely to how they feel about the effect. Take a seasoned drinker to another land and see how he responds. I guarantee you he will not jump with joy at his first taste of arak, pulque, marc, subrouska, or kava. Nor will he exalt at his first sip of an exotic concoction made by certain African tribes from banana mash. Your tongue will tell you whether you drink for the taste or in spite of it. Nevertheless, if you were to live in one of these lands with nothing else to do, never fear; in time your tongue would thirst for the strange liquid, too.

Apparently, then, liquor does not need thirst or taste to attract its followers. What it does do is *relax* you; it frees you for a time from your nagging inner self and helps make the world brighter; it heightens your pleasure and makes you feel good.

But is that the whole answer? I think not. For there appears to be among humans and other organisms a persistent and irradicable desire for both stimulation and narcosis. Why this universal disposition and compulsion should persist — not in one place or one time but in all places for all times — is worth pondering.

We must get one thing straightened out from the start. People today look for the same scientific measures of emotion, motivation and psychology in this area as they have come to expect in the physical sciences. Obviously they cannot be so easily provided. I can separate out a nerve reflex and test and control its responses to my heart's content; but I cannot take out the vast complex of human emotion and experience that go into thinking, feeling, comprehending and responding, and test them. And, in a way, although my curiosity is high, I am glad I cannot. For I sometimes feel as though the programmers and the packagers, the computers and the compulsives, the organizers and the organized, have stifled the breath of creativity that lurks in us all. Somehow the study of motivation and irrational human behavior, unleashed and given impetus by the Viennese maverick Sigmund Freud, who showed us things are not always what they seem to be, does not bend itself easily to old manners and methods. Perhaps this insistent desire to understand ourselves — and thereby, perhaps, to save ourselves — will one day produce the required pressure for new and adventurous methods. I sincerely hope so.

Whenever an activity or a particular form of human behavior is widespread, deep-seated and continuous, it has a practical meaning and use. This use may not be readily observable or understandable, even to the individual himself, but the behavior has purpose. This is true of any and all activities, no matter how dangerous, silly or purposeless they seem. For that reason, during stress our adrenal glands pour out the chemical hydrocortisone to prepare us for danger. Blood is drained from the surface of the body and pooled deep in body organs so as not to be lost easily; the heart beats faster while the blood pressure rises so that instant succor is made available to those parts in need. Sphincters are shut so elimination will not distract us from defending against danger; the flesh raises "goosebumps," the remnant of our bodily hair standing on end for added protection; the muscles become taut to absorb traumas more effectively and to go more rapidly into action; the mind is concentrated and alert to eliminate distractions and quickly respond to threat by fight or flight. Besides these responses to danger, the male has in his scrotum a neat reflex to control automatically the correct delicate temperature required by spermatazoa for survival (incidentally, while the sperm can tolerate a very high concentration of alcohol, it succumbs quickly to relatively small temperature variations); without the bearer being aware, his scrotum will snuggle the testes closer to his body for added warmth when the situation requires it, or the converse will occur when things get too warm. Furthermore, since we can now control our environmental temperature, our bodies no longer require their former hairy coat.

Old practices, like old body structures, seem sometimes very remote in meaning and mechanism; but when traced back to their beginnings, they are found invariably to be tied in with preservation, reproduction, and the evolution of the race to a so-called higher form. For that reason, those primitive religious rites that were used to ward off evil relate to modern religious rituals to ward off fear of the unknown. Indeed, all emotions — especially extremes of emotion — have ancient parentage and origins connected with the practical life. The dumb, blind rage of the primitive man who was robbed of his mate was essential if the species was to survive, and carries over to this day in some of the feelings manifested toward and by the cuckolded male.

Upon these observations are based my belief that we wish and hope for the capacity to attain extremes of stimulating excitement. By that I mean an exceptional, intense state of consciousness, or awareness, which is related intimately to the pleasure component of the old pleasure-pain mechanisms of organisms. The drive and eager desire for moments of such intense stimulation and increased awareness have, I believe, always belonged more to the strong, active, flexible individuals among us than to the weak and rigid. I further believe that the ability to permit yourself moments of increased awareness, when unfamiliar impulses and experiences are allowed to occur, may be one way to develop individuality and leadership and thus help promote progress as a whole. In other words, flexible persons invite fresh experiences into their lives, while the rigid struggle to keep them out. Both, of course, are generalities at either end of the spectrum; gradations are necessary and desirable from either end.

Now that I have presented you with this large proposition — that the ability to desire and tolerate moments of intense and unfamiliar awareness is a strong component of strong individuals — we can see how liquor might qualify. In the first place, remember that the practice of drinking did not come into existence in one place and then spread out over the world from there; it arose spontaneously in nearly every land. There is no substantial area of the earth that I know of which did not begin independently to produce, and continue to produce, some kind of beverage alcohol.

The desire for drink has been so keen, the quest for it so unremitting, and the use of it so continuous, that there can be little argument about its importance to individuals and societies. There has always been — and always will be — a need for some agent by which man can alter his inner being in relation to his environment. He can do this either by heightened awareness (or consciousness), or by heightened unawareness (or unconsciousness); either way, we can readily see how liquor fits quickly into either end of this diad of experience. Unless there is an unknown biological value to be accounted for in these responses, there is no way of explaining liquor's persistence across the flood of time. Perhaps its value can be seen by looking at the drinking technique of primitive man.

It is next to impossible for us, having so many different interests and means of excitement, to imagine what our savage ancestors thought of "heightened awareness" achieved through liquor. Nor can we conceive of the many uses he put it to. But I find it difficult to imagine what would have happened to our forebears without liquor. Perhaps they might not have survived at all — and even if they had, the result would have been markedly different from life on earth as we know it now.

Primitive man was unaware that liquor had use as a beverage alone. That came later. He drank liquor as a drug, because it gave him a feeling of freedom and expansion; it gave him a social enthusiasm and a high intensity of consciousness whereby he reached new levels of sensation. He became optimistic, confident, his life had richer meaning; he looked into a larger world, transcended his limitations, and gained a new conception of his powers. And when he was done, narcosis blotted out the flood. He drank, in other words, to get drunk.

Alcohol later developed within primitive cultures, as we have seen, as part of an agricultural complex. In each culture, at least one beverage assumed a mythological and sacred character, considered the life essence of the cereal god. Since the god was immortal, so became the partaker of the sacred drink, and drunkenness at feasts in honor of the grain god became a sacred duty. The Iroquois Indians used alcohol in the seventeenth century to stimulate their mystical faculties. They believed that the will of the spirits could be learned through visions and dreams, and they considered the temporary loss of mental control as the best way toward a more intimate touch with reality. A drunken trance, therefore, was regarded as a genuine metaphysical revelation. To the Iroquois, intoxication originally meant not flight, but search; not escape, but fulfillment; not loss of self, but discovery of self. It was a positive spiritual experience.

The liquor itself, guessing at its quality, must have almost killed them. Even so, it was apparently worth it. Primitive man did not know this feeling of expansion was unreal; it just happened. To him, this was no temporary vision, but a discovery of self in powerful perspective by which new ideas and new limits of conduct and development were set. Thus, instead of considering drunkenness immoral or in bad taste, it became a principal factor in mental, social and practical

life. It may even have helped socialize man and given
him religion. For liquor removed, temporarily, the innate suspicions of the mind; it paved the way for common thoughts and feelings. For once, primitive man
could look at foreign tribesmen without a weapon in
his hand. Indeed, at that epoch of evolution, when so-
cialization hung in the balance, alcohol may have provided *the* social impulse which decided whether man
was to form wider human groups or remain in that
narrow tribal furrow.

I can understand if you find it hard to believe that
liquor had this profound influence on man — but wait
patiently, until we have a chance to look into the full
scope of its uses. In primitive times, liquor influenced
all ceremonials, festivals, meetings, marriages, funerals,
dances, initiations, hospitalities, preparations for war,
consummations of peace, making of laws, care of the
sick — and, in a sense, even the creation of gods. Intoxication from liquor became a cult, a rite, during which
medicine, religion and law were conceived and born.

In medicine, the doctrine of stimulant and narcotic
reaches across the span of time. The life principle —
the soul — was thought to control the body; to cure
disease, therefore, this vital principle must be somehow
stimulated to greater effort. Although some of primitive man's ideas have been discarded during the course
of centuries, this is not one of them. Aristotle and Plato
believed it in their day, as did most of the celebrated
early physicians, including Galen and, much later,
Paracelsus.

Our modern pharmaceutical industry believes in it, too, judging by the enormous number of pills for pep, sleep, psychic energizing, and tranquilizing that are sold. The success of the patent-medicine industry also depends almost universally upon alcohol as one of the active ingredients in its products. (You remember in Chapter 3 how my aunt was aided by a tonic laced with a lot of alcohol. Well, when I was an interne, I had a patient who never imbibed, but had a persistent nagging cough which required frequent heavy doses of a patent-medicine cough syrup. Although he complained bitterly at the annoyance of the cough and the need for medicine, no other medication could be as effective as the one he'd taken for years. You can guess that it had a good amount of alcohol in its formula!)

Perhaps the strong modern emphasis on narcosis, or diminished awareness through tranquilization, is simply a reflection of the flood of unfamiliar impulses that now engulfs us. In our hurry-up existence — where we sniff instead of savor, gulp instead of sip, eat instead of dine, fornicate instead of love — perhaps the dulling of one's senses by tranquilizers has become essential.

The religious connection between liquor and intoxication is the clearest of all. To begin with, intoxication itself was once a religious rite (it was actually supposed to have founded one of the first organized religions, shamanism). The close identity of intoxication with religious fervor is responsible, indeed, for the existence of intoxication cults in almost all known primitive tribes. To them, far from being regarded as sinful or irreligious, drunkenness was an integral part of the worshiping experience and, in many cases, was prescribed by the religion itself.

To primitive man this was entirely logical. The sense of increased power and the ecstatic sensation which liquor provided brought him closer to the divine level and gave him the courage to converse with his gods. Remnants of liquor and religion, like rudimentary organs of the body, continue in today's religions. Although the modern communion seems a far cry from the ancient drunken soma of India, none of the transitional steps are missing to prove the common ancestral root in primitive intoxication rites. Divine frenzy was much sought after and required long training to produce hysterical reactions. Young candidates for religious training were chosen from among the most constitutionally sensitive and excitable; fits, wailing and strange body movements were voluntarily induced for religious purposes, which illustrates another custom that did not entirely die with primitive man.

Some will no doubt scoff at such "uncivilized" worship, but I sometimes wonder if our drunken primitive ancestors did not feel more attuned to god and religion than many of our sober modern-day mechanistic worshipers.

But if primitive man learned something about the joys of intoxication, he discovered its dangers as well. Liquor and intoxication caused laws and limits to be introduced. To be wrapped in the bosom of intoxication meant decreased capacity for battle, hence increased danger from attack. Liquor use had to be controlled. Perhaps here, in the dark recesses of our ancestry, did the moral attitudes against drink first stir.

Liquor, of course, has its opposite effect. In fact, alcohol is the only natural drug which can supply both conditions; for after the heightened awareness and increased sensation come the *unawareness* and *decreased* sensation. Narcosis sits on the other end of the scale waiting for the drive toward awareness to subside. Awareness is an expression of the will to live, to create, to act; unawareness is an expression of fatigue, an urge for rest from an excessively stimulating environment. Both expressions appear each day in everyone, awake and asleep. They can appear and predominate in an individual in the course of a few years; and they can appear and predominate in a nation in the course of a few centuries.

The Russians are a good example. For centuries the mass of Russian people lived under the rigid, harsh rule of the czars. And then, although you may regret it, the October Revolution of 1917 set in motion a new stimulation and awareness. In less than fifty years, the Russian people have changed from a herd of rigid "existers" to a people who are flexible, aware and alive. When I visited the Soviet Union in 1960, I could not help but be impressed with the dynamic drive and vitality of the people. They had self-respect and self-possession. They were aware and interested. In short, they knew where they were going. You may not like my example, but unless you wear extra thick blinders, you cannot help but admire the way this downtrodden, defeated people has become a vital world power in a very short time.

This human striving for flexible awareness is basically the love of life and the hunger for more of it. In the individual and within the group, it is the raw meat of enthusiasm. Here lies the desire to tap untried personal potentials and pleasures, and so to marshal new powers and extended capacities in a way never accomplishable by rigidity and moderation. Flexible awareness is a spirit that is apparently an essential ingredient of crude courage and strength, both of which become transformed and polished. Where there is no force, there is no growth; where there is no striving for awareness, there is no life; and where there is no change, there is no culture.

Man must have some challenge and even some threat; he must test his environment and have it push back against him so the boundaries of his being are delineated. Without such encounters, the self tends not to be determined and one's touch with life becomes fragmentary. The person whose boundaries are fuzzy merely gets pushed along by the currents of the day, piling on and collecting more materials which control him rather than he controls them. Have you ever noted the distress of a housewife whose dishwasher is unworkable, and there's no one around who knows how to repair it? And are you not acquainted with the family in despair because the television set is inoperable, and they stare dumbly at this seducing monster whose innards they do not understand?

I believe, as do many others, that these states of high intensity of awareness are responsible for much of the higher order of thinking in man's mental evolution; and further, that these states, when organized and under control, are the power and tension behind long-continued concentration. For this reason, an Einstein is seemingly "absentminded" or unaware of the sundry stimuli that annoy the rest of us. I have had close personal contact with a man such as Einstein: the late Norbert Wiener, who was an old and very close friend of mine. Although I must resist the temptation to tell you more about him (it will have to wait for another time, and perhaps another book), a brief vignette may illustrate the point. Norbert could be absorbed completely in thinking through the most complicated abstraction in the midst of activities and stimuli that could seduce the lot of us. His catnaps, at strange hours in strange places, were not peculiar to him but are as common to the Edisons as they are to the Einsteins. (Norbert's concentration, so helpful to him, was also helpful to me on occasion; it permitted me to boost my ego by beating him at chess. Not that I was the superior player; no, he would concentrate so intently on parlaying his pieces into devilishly clever and original attacks that he forgot I was less brilliantly but busily attacking.)

Although my friend's ability to concentrate and

achieve high states of intensity of awareness was great, he also required throughout his lifetime an inordinate amount of rest and replenishment. The replenishment and release come from the ultimate onset of awareness; both states — heightened awareness and narcosis — are thus considered psychological kin, using similar mechanisms of the nervous system.

I also believe that these states of awareness and unawareness, and the craving to attain them, have been an important instrument in man's struggle for survival. Individuals in a society whose nervous and emotional organization is eager for (and capable of) intense, sustained action are in the best position to provide new answers for new problems. The striving for awareness characterizes all people and nations in dominant roles and is most marked during periods of rapid growth. Example after example appears — the period before the cult of Dionysus in Greece, before the Renaissance, before the years of most rapid acceleration in the United States, and so forth. Such vigorous spirit and the use of liquor lie in the same bed: both can be expressions of mental and physical virility. During the temporary relaxation of rigidity and reality, the life scope is widened and new enthusiasms are created. It is then that the crudeness in growth is transformed and polished into a bright new social era.

One bit of confirmation about liquor and increased awareness is contained in the study of Harvard sociologist Anne Roe among a group of artists. Some reported liquor as a stimulus to creative work, while others indicated its indirect effect on painting through relaxation. Tension relief apparently promotes a state in which new work can be conceived and old work finished.

To most of you who are reading this book, liquor drinking falls principally under the heading of *increasing awareness*. The normal man drinks to heighten pleasure and enthusiasm — to intensify, to relate, to communicate, to feel, to let go, to socialize, to link arms with bores. Reality is a wonderful though painful adventure, and the only one he has. But after all, too much of anything becomes tiresome; once in a while (or more often, depending on his personality) he must masquerade his personal reality by splashing loud colors on it. A man I know well and admire is one whom I would classify as a "benevolent misanthrope." He does not like being around too many people because he senses the falseness, ugliness and futility in much of what they say and do. But let my friend have a couple of martinis and how the picture changes! The grays and blacks, the harsh and ugly realities of his misanthropy rapidly disappear and he splashes on his canvas of perception bright, lively colors. The women are all beautiful, the men handsome, dedicated and strong; life is full of pure pleasure and little pain. The profuse statements of his love of life and his joy in living after a little liquor are, for me, always evidence of how this man's reality has undergone a healthy, temporary change.

I am not saying that normal man never takes a drink to diminish his awareness. Under certain conditions he might. The problem drinker on the other hand, drinks for unawareness exclusively. He is a human island in a sea of alcohol, and he finds his haven in narcosis — the opposite of the desire for more life. For example, a patient of mine, who was at the time sober, took his wife one day to the skid row part of town. The wife was aghast at the sight of prostrate bodies lying in stuporous poses in scores of doorways. What horrified her more — and illustrates the drive to narcosis which typifies the problem drinkers — was her husband's voice saying, "You know, dear, you cannot imagine how much I envy them their oblivion!"

As with those who suffer from rigor mortis of spirit, these unlucky ones seek refuge from all intense states, from strenuousness and vigor. The constant theme is rest and escape, and the goal is a hiding place from the world. Unfortunately for the problem drinker and the rigid soul (the one, remember, who wants to keep new experiences out) this is not so easily accomplished, for they are merely hiding from themselves. Still, they can manage to make their presence known; the rigid person, who has not had much pleasure out of life, is hell-bent on making sure no one else has any for fear he will learn that life is passing him by. Such people must have things "just so," and anything unplanned or unprepared for is taboo. I have seen this reaction especially when I have lived or traveled in other countries. Many of my fellow Americans go to another country seeking the comforts and values of home. I cannot understand why they bother to go. If they do not want to learn and experience new modes and manners, they must spend all that money merely to say they've been. Unfortunately, too many people spend their entire lives ravaged by the pain of *being* and the dread of *not being;* most people never realize they are living at half their potential. As with the rigid reformer, the problem drinker has a horrible time of it, too. Married to his faithless mistress, alcohol, he is a walking blank, and he has had no fun getting there. On the contrary, it is rough. For him, heightened awareness through alcohol provides only sharper edges to his personal disturbances, which may explain why he wants to get drunk so quickly — and why he hates to sober up.

Now, the normal drinker occasionally strives for unawareness, too, but the difference lies in the fact that he wants to come back. Let me hastily reassure you, however, that I am not referring to the tired man who drinks to relax after a hard day's work. He seeks merely to dim reality by injecting vividness into the moment. Although this can be called escape, it is different from avoiding reality; it is intensification of the brightness in one's reality. When we drink to narcotize ourselves, however, we are "escaping" the same as the problem drinker, but the reasons are outside ourselves. Some grief, pain, injury or situation has occurred which may, in time, be alleviated; but if alleviation does not come and we have no other methods of response, we may go on to degeneration.

This same effect may be likened to the life of a nation, the classical example being Japan. Because of external threat, the Japanese people were essentially isolated from the rest of the world on this planet for three hundred years and thereby, as a nation they were figuratively narcotized (no new or outside experiences were ever allowed in). The ample evidence we have is that the Shogunate dictatorships during this period were destroying any creative force that may have remained alive. While Admiral Perry and the United States Navy, by forcing Japan to end its isolation and narcosis, permitted the nation to burst forth as a world power, the unawareness of the people was perpetuated by a moral dictatorship demanding conformity to the divinity of the Emperor. And when, finally, a bit of independent force exploded among the Japanese, the pendulum swung to brutality and destructiveness.

As a Japanese psychologist told me when I visited there, "Although we [the Japanese] have imitated many undesirable customs and values of Americans, you have also allowed us to respect ourselves as individuals with rights and not as inanimate, insignificant pieces to serve a mortal god. With our ability to have new stimuli and new experiences, our creativity and vitality abound." And we all know how vigorously the Japanese are progressing now that they have shed their shackles of control and conformity.

Strength, crudeness and enthusiasms combine to

create growth and build a nation. During such periods there is an increased sense of awareness and flexibility similar to that achieved with liquor. Then gradually national life becomes more intricate and complex. There is emigration toward centers of progress and greater flux among classes. Behavior becomes stereotyped; individuality is despised and conformity reigns. The more complex the problems, the greater the striving for simple answers. As the stagnation grows, adjustment becomes increasingly difficult. Rather than the spirit searching for heightened awareness, the flooded soul seeks solace in narcosis. And like a cancer, the narcosis grows. Unless the situation is alleviated (which, in national life, means replenishment from outside forces), the drive toward rigid unawareness spreads out and soon all growth is stifled.

In America today there is this desire to stifle new growth (I do not mean the growth and proliferation of new products, which tend only to minimize testing our environment). We are frightened by new ideas, new plans, changes in the routine. Instead of looking at them to see if they might have any possible worth to our society, we shut our collective eyes by draping threatening labels or slogans upon them.

As I pointed out in my brief description of Americans abroad, if we don't go to look and learn, we ultimately will die. For as Frank M. Colby said: "Every man ought to be inquisitive through every hour of his great adventure down to the day when he shall no longer cast a shadow in the sun. For if he dies without a question in his heart, what excuse is there for his continuance?" Like the business that does not grow and stays still with its old ways, the nation which does not press for new ideas and experience from within and without its borders must in time stagnate and lose its vital power.

Let us for the moment review the premises we have put forth regarding the impulse toward increased awareness, and how liquor historically and persistently fits into the picture. First, I have stated that any continuous and widespread aspect of human behavior has a practical use in the development of people and nations, and that the striving for increased awareness is surely a continuous, widespread aspect of behavior. Liquor became a popular agent for increasing awareness because of its ready accessibility, and because it can both increase and decrease consciousness. Further, I believe that liquor has aided the advance of mankind and has had some parentage in the establishment of manners, sciences and gods.

Can you imagine how many people will scoff at that! Liquor of positive use to mankind? Impossible. Earlier, I mentioned the fact that there was a flood of liquor literature existing in this country, most of it directed to pointing out the negative side of the liquor story. The focus is ever on the ravages from alcoholism, but implicit in many of the writings (and even more in the attitudes of people) is that the desire for, and enjoyment of, drinking is due to total depravity or original sin. True, since the death of prohibition in the United States and the overt acceptance of drinking, the messages of disapproval have had to be couched in different terms. The myths, however, go merrily on and the fears foment.

We must discuss reformers and do-gooders because, as one of the many paradoxes of life, even they seek stimulation (but not awareness). Now we might all feel more sympathetic toward reformers, do-gooders and pleasure-killers if we generally recognized them for what they really are: seekers of stimulation instead of self-sacrificers giving their lives to relieve the suffering of others. (The drinker gets no such noble label; he is just a drinker.) The reformer and the do-gooder — those who want to knock us all into line — use fanaticism and asceticism to increase their sense of stimulation. These people are so anxious to go out and assail life with determination, persistence and vigor that they stimulate themselves into a feeling of divine personal greatness and importance not too far removed from that of the primitives I spoke of before. Under such protection, the ability to impose one's will and "do good" with this new personal power is exhilarating. Whether or not the objectives become distorted, or the goals no longer exist, or the vision fails to pan out, the desire is the same.

We can see this when we look at prohibition movements. In 1912, Toronto had a law forbidding alcohol sale from Friday at seven o'clock until Monday morning, and it was reported there were never so many drunkards on the street as on Sunday. Norway, Sweden, Russia, Turkey — all have tried liquor prohibitions in modern times, and the ancient history of prohibition is as long as the history of drink. But none of them can hold a candle to the American experiment. Perhaps this is as it should be. An Englishman once remarked that there are more fools in the United States than in any other country in the world. That shouldn't surprise anyone: there is also more of everything else here. Therefore, the noble experiment in prohibition in the United States was, fittingly, the loudest, most spectacular and most costly — and terminated in the most mammoth failure. The reformers of that day were no weaklings without drive. They had unity, coherence, purpose, emphasis and a primitive excitement similar to what one expects from a nation at its stage of greatest vitality and most rapid growth.

But liquor use is so deeply engrained in the nature of man that it took those reformers nearly a hundred years to accomplish their goal. For the beginnings of this last dry movement were in the 1820's. What started it rolling on its merry way was what starts many a movement: empty pews in churches. A new slogan, a new impetus was needed and they chose "temperance." Of course, like all stiflers, they did not mean temperance at all, but total abolition. The reformers of that day wanted strong doses of medicine swallowed for a symptom, without so much as a nod to find out if, in fact, there existed a malady at all. They wanted laws. But when they had achieved them, only to realize the laws were ineffective because they went against the inner desires of the populace, their efforts became even more strident.

The evils of aggressive teetotalism did not become apparent until the United States experiment. The liquor reformers did not have a ghost of a chance, of course, but fanatic excitement like theirs can survive only in an uncompromising atmosphere. In the Middle Ages it was hereticism; in the early 1900's it was liquor; lately it has been communism. For the fearful, for the reformer, one signpost is all that is required for focus. Give him a cause or a leader and he will march with righteous vigor to do battle against anything that is new, untried or threatening. For the exponents of rigidity, liquor has always been a special offender and a rallying post. They have fought for its elimination to the end and have put up a great battle — and, as usual, they have caused everybody a great deal of trouble.

The reformer against liquor, as the reformer against progress and pleasure, is always a fighter and always makes his presence felt in a big way, even though the fight is hopeless. This is precisely why he is so dangerous. To fight against (and at one time actually to legislate against) a useful human practice many millenia old, without knowledge of its role and importance, is not only irrational but causes evils it fancies it is curing, or puts worse ones in their place. Most do-gooders will plead innocent to such charges, but only because they have been blinded by personal urge. Nevertheless, they have been responsible for undesirable circumstances. For example, since alcohol production got out of the hands of the church, the commercial liquor industry has been frequently associated with certain disreputable elements. Instead of trying to improve that situation, the reformers have set up a sustained din against the evils of liquor that has drowned out the voices feebly attempting to create perspective and thereby convinced the majority that the evils must be real. Long ago the propaganda was planted that no respectable person would have anything to do with liquor, that only ghouls who preyed on human weakness would stoop to make money from it. To this day, in the United States, liquor may not contaminate the mails, nor be advertised in most media, nor be sold to anyone under a certain chronological age of incorruptibility (this same lack of respect for dealing with sales of liquor may be related to the fact that the Irish Catholic had a monopoly in the "retail spirituous trade," and perhaps explains the strong prejudice in America against the Irish Catholic until John F. Kennedy came along).

We have now realized that prohibition can only have the effect of making people drink more, and of the worst kind of drink. High taxation of liquor is probably the best answer, and although some of us feel that it is unfair to tax beer, wine and spirits so heavily, we can at least feel with satisfaction that upon us, and our lifted glasses, the budget gets balanced.

9

Liquor and You

In understanding the *why* of liquor, many parts must
be provided for the whole. Although we examine them
as if they are static, single entities, they are in fact
dynamic, interrelated, multiple forces. When we talk
about psychology we talk about the brain — and the
brain, remember, is where alcohol importantly hits. We
ought to begin this part of our examination, therefore,
with a description of what liquor actually does to the
brain, and how it functions to produce this effect.

The nature and workings of the human nervous
system in providing our total contact with the world is
interesting in itself, and it is man's ability to modify
these workings that causes the existence of liquor. All
of our incoming sensations travel up sensory nerve
fibers to the spinal cord, then up the spinal cord to report to the general manager, which is the cerebral
cortex. The nervous system is often described as a
chain of switchboards because there are junctions all

along the way which redistribute the energy of the incoming stimulus. This action, called "threshold resistance," slows the stimulus down, and it is this which
alcohol increases. In other words, alcohol slows down
incoming sensations to a point below the natural speed
(and sometimes prevents sensations from entering the
brain entirely). In the meantime, liquor has befuddled
the general manager so badly that many sensations
which do get through stand little chance of being
noticed.

There is, however, an even greater curiosity in the
effect of alcohol on the nervous system. It is an intruder
and is, of course, resisted; it relies on the fact that certain areas of the brain are stouter and more resistant
than others. These areas and functions hang on longer,
which means that different areas of the body blank
out at different times. Thus the effect of alcohol is like
a natural vivisection, in which the body is figuratively
cut into segments. It works essentially in the same order, beginning at the top of the head and moving
down. The higher brain, the cerebral cortex, goes first —
it hasn't been with us long, evolutionally, and is not so
well integrated and entrenched. The next to go is the
sensory function, followed by the motor function
(which controls the ability for movement).

And so the narcosis descends, until finally it reaches
the oldest levels of the brain. Here our most vital body
activities are controlled; we have had them a long time
and they show a great deal of stamina. Because of them
the intestines, bladder and heart all continue to con-

tract, and the respiratory reflex drags in the oxygen, allowing you to breathe long after the rest of your body is drugged to helpless coma. Alcohol can finally get these strong ones, too, but it has to build up its blood concentration to the lethal limit. It has to kill you to do it.

You do not often meet people who care to drink like that; dimming the cortex and cutting out certain psychic factors usually suffices. In any case, it is not necessary to see a man drink himself to death in order to observe the interesting spectacle I am about to describe. For it is under the influence of alcohol that we are a witness to the retracing of the whole life history of the race — in one man, in one evening — all the way back down the evolutionary stairway. First, his herd-group tendencies disappear (these are the last tendencies man has acquired and are recognizable as the following: consideration of other people, restraints, refinements and niceties). Next to go are anxiety, prudence, modesty, reserve, and all the rest of what psychologists call "group logic," the orthodox rules of group or civilized conduct. Older, more basic impulses push up from below: jerky speech, roaring laughter, excessive sentimentality. By now he has gone a good way down; he has left the herd and is imitating the procedures of the hulking man with the one-inch forehead who was his forebear. Psychically he is roving alone — coarse, reckless, predatory, dangerous, and possibly criminal, because the criminal life of today comes close to the normal life of primitive man.

Please understand that I am not referring to you and me — not necessarily, that is. I am referring to anybody who will sit down and drink a quart or more of whiskey. There are no exceptions to the fact that that is all it takes to qualify, because this has been a description of the action of alcohol in the human brain per se. But why should anyone want to get into a state like that? What perverse part of human nature causes this? Why on earth should the race, after millions of years of struggling up from caves and jungles, deliberately wish to return, even temporarily, as indeed it seems bent on doing?

This compulsion is shown in other habits beside drinking liquor (which is simply the surest, safest, quickest and cheapest). It is shown in both adult sport and the play of children. Some psychologists stress the child's-play example because the child has not been taught what is supposed to be fun and therefore makes his selection spontaneously. He selects running, rolling, wrestling, climbing, digging, throwing, yelling, hitting, roving. Though he knows nothing about enforced monotony, he instinctively rebels against all activities dictated by the last developed portion of his mind, such as school and chores and any routine that requires concentration. He has selected the brain's oldest pathway because it is the best worn and easiest.

The adult, who has had a taste of the discipline of his new brain, seeks these reversionary activities even more avidly — and at almost any expense and discomfort. Not only does he cherish the more violent physical sports, but he screams his lungs out at fights and wrestling matches; moreover, he will live in a tent, sleep on the ground, cook over an open fire, or search out the darkest woods and the deepest waters. He calls this "getting back to nature" and he is calling it right. Or perhaps he should call it second nature (but that is not right, because it came first). Hunting, camping, swimming, dancing, horse racing and yachting all pull in the opposite mental direction from the urge to build and advance, to which we owe our progress. They seem so natural because they are, literally, just that; but a synonym for natural is primitive, and what we are doing when we enjoy them is tugging toward the one-inch forehead, away from the tyrant of incentive. The procedure is seldom comfortable and sometimes not very beautiful, but we love it and need it. The point is, why? The answer may well be the point of this entire book.

Human progress strives in a definite and unchanging direction — which is *up*. Up from nomadic simplicity and ignorance and irresponsibility to larger growing groups and more complex life levels and more responsibility to others. This is the direction, but the movement is oscillating. Man's newer brain tires quickly; he must swing back and rest it by stressing his use of the older way of things. For bad or good, however, it is the new brain, and the higher psychical process it produces, that is wholly responsible for progress. The effect is an endless chain, because the higher it drives us the higher must become its own development. Perhaps it began as a natural protective mechanism, but nobody knows; nor can anyone tell whether the direction is right, or whether it is the one we are after, since we are never going to arrive.

But there it is, and we want it, as any human being can prove to his own satisfaction simply by trying to live the rest of his days in even a semiprimitive environment. It wouldn't be the loss of comforts and luxuries — although he would miss these plentifully for a while — but the loss of tension that would bore him to death, that and his inability to obey the new devil, *cerebral cortex,* which begins with a little switch and builds up to a bullwhip. Soon the very pressures he had hidden from (and thinks he does not want) would recover their strength, find him and call him back.

Because we exist in a day when all the untidy threats to comfort (and strangely enough, to pleasure) are removed, we wonder where the living is. Fuzzless peaches, seedless grapes, shiftless cars, caffeine-free coffee and odorless liquor are pressing on the populace to prevent the pain of living. All these efforts on behalf of removing the sting of challenge and the pleasure of the unknown are in the direction of playing it safe. They are also strongly in the direction of non-living. It may be this non-living, this loss of stress on the individual and society, that leads to the many existing dissatisfactions present in our world. It is as if, once all discomfort (and all stimulus to progress) has disappeared, we create more powerful means of self-destruction to remind us of our unattended, innate, evolutionary need to ascend.

I'm not saying that being satisfied is bad per se; I do say that being satisfied permanently is death. Without new perspectives, new goals, new questions, new challenges, new frictions, how do we know where we are, where we've been, and where we want to go?

Now, this "new brain" we have been discussing occupies the top spot in the psychology of alcohol because it, like any newborn, needs more rest than any other part — *and alcohol has the ability to go directly to it and put it to sleep.* The new brain is a sprinter, not a miler, and its unique powers of intense concentration tire more quickly than the functions of the older brain. It cannot go on working continuously, even through the waking hours. More than one realizes, nature brings reverie daily through fantasy life, forcing us to devise our own artificial means of resting the higher processes while still keeping the lower ones busy.

So mankind, like a base-runner trapped stealing a base, seems to be caught between opposing forces: ceaseless progress and unfailing rest. His new brain takes care of the former, and as the pressure quickens he must learn for himself more and more ways of taking care of the latter. Fortunately, man has a highly developed curiosity and a constant temptation to swing to extremes, to venture wider in each direction. This has been one of his racial elevators. His curiosity is innate and expresses itself personally as well as externally. Man likes to try experiments on himself; his interest in modifications of his body, mental and physical, is ingrained in his behavior pattern. In summer he likes to lie in the sunshine, trying to recover the dark skin he has lost. Then he grows tired of this and seeks the opposite extreme. He likes the far ends, the swing back and forth taking in greater and greater territory. Even his body economy — psychological and physiological — is founded on a principle of alternating phases: activity and inactivity, tension and rest. His new brain pulls him forever *toward* the tension, *toward* ambition and concentration; his modification instinct swings him *back* — to rest and change and re-creation.

This cerebral cortex, this new brain, is a hundred million or so years old, but like everything else it had to evolve from a rudimentary form. By the standards of evolution, it has made very good time; it has risen up comparatively recently, and already it has gained control. Probably its first traces showed up in the brain of the dawn man, when he was first learning to live peacefully with his fellows in the same clearing. He was learning patience, which requires concentration. It is this tension of concentration — the ability to put the mind on something and keep it there — which demarcates man from animal and civilized man from savage. The dawn man knew tension, of course, because his life was complex compared to that of the beasts. Probably this stress gap was as great as was civilized man's compared to the savage, or the northern races compared to the southern. Today, this stress —

the necessity for "swing-back" and cerebral rest — is greatest among people in urban areas.

Ah, but then we have liquor.

We have now put a lot of jigsaw-puzzle pieces in place and have, I trust, provided some reasons for the striving for excitement, for increased awareness and narcosis, even in lower forms of life. In short, we have defined the unrelenting drive and counterdrive of evolution and devolution: the drive upward to higher, dryer, safer ground and the counterdrive back to the ambitionless primordial ooze. This conflictive situation explains why a need for awareness and excitement sprang up in primitive life; it also explains the seeming incongruity of unquenchable liquor thirst in a simple, hardy man with no complexes. Excitement and increased awareness, these raised him up, gave him new visions and high personal concepts, a belief and confidence in the supernatural and the courage to try. The more vigorous the people, the nation or the individual — those whose higher brains are capable of greater intensity and thus demand the more certain swing-back — the more the need for stimulation and rest.

But suppose there is an overabundance of stimulation, excitement and awareness, more than can be handled, such that the tension becomes unbearable and the need for sedation heightens? Here may I say emphatically that today, here and now, we need to fear far more the sedative, tranquilizing drive than its opposite. Whereas liquor in excess produces disturbing, obvious behavior, readily noted and dealt with by society, such is not the case with tranquilization. No one is too upset by an easily manipulated vegetable or the constantly well behaved; even though all creative drive is gone, and all protective awareness has flown with the pills, persons so inundated seem preferable to the sodden. To my mind, it is merely a question of which evil is the greater: an excess of stimulation or an excess of sedation.

There are other positive aspects in the use of liquor since the dawn of man. Think what it does for the critical, the shy, the glum, the bundle-of-nerves, the fearful, the unsocial, the misanthrope. And consider, too, how it helps the more brilliant person in less gifted company, or the brilliant person who is emotionally incapable of the broadening experience of close human contact. Liquor levels and humanizes them all; nothing else I know of has yet been discovered that does the job quite as well.

You may not think this leveling and humanizing is important. But I do. It is important because it aids emotional communication between people; under the frenzied conditions of our "status-cursed, urban-suburban treadmill," according to pharmacologist Chauncy D. Leake: "Liquor drinking at the end of an emotionally gruelling day may have a real civilizing effect on the overtense, overwrought, overanxious, and overirritable husband who comes seeking rest and peace in his own home. Here the civilizing effects (of moderate amounts) will really perform wonders in helping husbands and wives to feel tolerant and understanding of each other. These amenities help adults generally to adjust themselves in a socially acceptable way to the stresses of our complex social situation."

Before the advent of the cerebral cortex, of course, such differences in mental attributes were not noticeable. Well, you should know by now what liquor does to the cerebral cortex. Thus does man return to the ancient clearing, his old common meeting ground, without his inner self-critic. Gone is the harshness of criticism, or the feelings of inferiority, of weakness and inadequacy. He becomes assertive; and even though, unlike primitive man, he realizes the next day that it is not entirely the whole truth, he cannot help but feel that it was not entirely false either. He may have gone a bit too far and regret it some — but at least he was there.

A number of years ago an American rhetorician wrote that a couple of drinks might make a man democratic, but that at the bottom of every glass *thereafter* lie superiority and aloofness. I can see the superiority, but not the aloofness. Why else is he around? It is difficult to test one's new strength if one remains aloof. Of course, people will point at a solitary drinker in the dark recesses of his abode and say, "What about him?" The individual who regularly drinks by himself is not using alcohol as it should be used; he is using it to treat himself. As I noted earlier, the lawyer who is his own lawyer and the physician who is his own physician have fools for legal and medical advisers. The person who drinks alone is treating himself on short diagnosis and is likewise a fool.

Some drinkers try to prove the increased strength they think alcohol has given them, although there is little evidence that liquor actually increases strength or efficiency at all. It may help one's efficiency at work so that routine jobs, instead of being looked forward to with boredom, will appear more interesting and be more pleasantly anticipated. We might assume that a glass of liquor in the morning before a day's work does impair work efficiency, but that does not mean that a glass of sherry, a martini, or some wine taken the night before, after an exhausting day, will necessarily impair one's efficiency on the following day. If liquor can overcome and suppress man's awareness of the little miseries and drudgeries in life, and thus set free and strengthen his enthusiasm for whatever dominant ideas he may cherish, and if it can lubricate the frictions and pains and bring back once again the feeling of unity and freedom of flow, then humans would be fools to ignore this aid to civilization.

One day, while pushing to reach my deadline for the completion of this manuscript, I half noticed that my body felt itchy. I was too busy to care really until my vanity was threatened: without apparent cause, my upper lip suddenly ballooned! My own physician was forced to conclude it was "something emotional" and

I tended to agree with him. In telling this to an acquaintance, her response was: "But I thought all psychiatrists were supposed to be well adjusted!"

Now if, as this lady intimated, the term *well adjusted* means "not having emotions" or "not responding to stress," then the only possible well-adjusted person is a corpse. And who, with all the great potential there is for really living, wants to be a corpse — even a well-adjusted one? Indeed, the effect of anxiety and conflict on the production of human ills is a much-discussed subject, oftentimes among the lay more than the professional groups. We know our mind can produce, or importantly influence, certain bodily behaviors. I am not talking about "imagined" illnesses, either, but some common, serious disturbances that derive from our inability to "let go." In more vigorous people, the greater capacity for work exacts a proportionately more effective cortical relaxation. Frequent vacations and long journeys can do it, provided you leave your worries at home, but such journeys take time.

Alcohol can do it in an evening.

When sober, the world contracts and one lives with the word "don't." When drinking, the world expands and one knows the word "do." We must not forget that our people in power — in government and big business — use a lot of liquor. Can you imagine what a diplomatic party would be like without it? Or a Presidential party? Or a business meeting in a social situation? I can assure you liquor is an essential guest at these functions. And why not?

But many of my colleagues — lay, professional and patient alike — recurrently warn that liquor is an escape. It certainly is. Why should escape be spoken of as something dangerous and somehow contemptible, like a flight from well-deserved punishment? There are all kinds of escapes; we need to know first what sort of escape is meant, and how long the escapee wants to remain that way. If you don't think we are all busy escaping in this society of ours, watch the response of people meeting a psychiatrist. They recoil playfully, humorously reassuring themselves that he will not delve too deeply and come up with one of those inner secrets they prefer to escape from.

As an example, I had the good fortune during a recent airline flight to be seated next to one of our state's representatives to the Miss America Pageant. This young lady had not won, but she had done exceptionally well and was in a rightfully exuberant state. I must confess that I was a trifle exuberant, too — picture for a moment, if you will, a middle-aged man who was the envy of every young fellow on that large jet! In my expansiveness (and perhaps in an attempt to hold her attention from the younger men), I divulged my professional specialty to her, something I ordinarily never do for fear of being drowned by boredom and confessional.

This young lady made the usual nervous, silly laugh and said, "Why don't you psychoanalyze me?" Before I could give an answer, she assured me that she really didn't want me to. Instead, she talked at great length about herself and her family, and I was soon aware that any word or expression that suggested I might be making an interpretation or judgment would have caused her to return swiftly to her book. So I listened carefully and looked intently — after all, my eyes are not so tired that I cannot appreciate a thing of beauty.

In any story about liquor not specifically addressed to the problem drinker, there are times when it becomes impossible to leave him out. This is not surprising. In an area where the warnings have been dire, the myths die hard. It is natural for people who drink liquor to wonder sometimes whether they might not be problem drinkers, or might become so, or simply whether they are drinking too much. Specialists pass too easily over this query; they forget that the overwhelming majority who drink are not, and never will be, problem drinkers. And yet I have not known one person who drinks, no matter how little, who hasn't thought about this. As a matter of fact, I never knew a teetotaler who didn't, at one time or another, wonder whether he might become a problem drinker should he ever partake of the stuff.

I read in a newspaper column of a man who had written to a "medical columnist" for advice about his drinking behavior. He had had two scotches before dinner each night for the thirty years of his married life and his wife was now afraid that he might become an alcoholic and need ever increasing amounts of liquor. The man reported that he definitely had not increased the amount and had no desire to do so; but, since his wife's persistence had raised doubts in his mind, he was writing to find out whether or not he ought to give up liquor. The good doctor reassured him that it was fine for him to go on enjoying his scotches before dinner. Had I been asked, I would have also added a suggestion that perhaps it might help if the wife joined her husband with a drink!

The social drinker uses liquor to exaggerate, to add new zest to a reality he has been eons creating, and which he normally finds exciting and enjoyable. Once in a while, though, he seeks to sharpen his view of reality. The problem drinker, on the other hand, is emotionally ill. He dreads even a glimpse of daily reality, but liquor can narcotize his inner pain and dull the edge of reality. Thus, both social and problem drinker use liquor for escape — but for totally opposite reasons.

Earlier I noted that the sober alcoholic envies the oblivion of the stuporous, which is the most serious level of problem drinking. But how about the problem drinker who has to take alcohol to change his reality and bolster his courage to plead a case in court, or speak before an audience, or fly on an airplane? Such a man needs to change his inner and outer reality in order to go on. I had a teacher when I was in the seventh grade who took nips all day long from a bottle in his desk; even then, I wondered what was so bad about his life that he had to drink so often. I never found out, but he was a nice man, a real human being, and I've never forgotten him or his plight.

Another phenomenon peculiar to the problem drinker is the fact that, after treatment, he will frequently discover that he does not — and has never — liked liquor itself at all! For years he had hungered for its narcotic effect, for the oblivion from reality which he sought; but liquor itself had no associations of pleasure, happiness or communication for him. He literally hated the stuff.

Such responses make one wonder why people always fret about "getting the habit"; they also make one wonder precisely what role habit plays in the use of alcohol. Simply stated, an action has to be performed many times before it can be called a habit. Habit, therefore, can have nothing to do with *procuring* the effect, since that can be accomplished with the first drink. Further, a habit is supposed to be an established tendency to repeat a certain act in a certain way. For the problem drinker, one can see how liquor, which leads to oblivion, could become the easy way; each time he starts along the same path, the tendency to repeat the performance must grow.

True, the tendency to overindulge in all things is a general human failing. But how about those of you who have partaken of alcohol foolishly the night before? Do you rush to drink again? I daresay you cannot stand the stuff, and you are perfectly willing to admit it. But time — that great healer of heart, body, mind and memory — will make you forget the occasion when you drank for the wrong reasons in the wrong manner. Is this a way to start a habit? I think not. For the problem drinker, the pain spiraling up from within is of such intensity and requires such relief that the memory of an unpleasant liquor experience evaporates all too rapidly and he begins again.

There is nothing I know of that addicts one, physiologically, to liquor except prolonged, copious use. This is not surprising, for I have seen people with signs of withdrawal after prolonged, copious use of almost any drug, including aspirin. I know of people who became addicted to morphine after a single large dose; but I know of no one who was ever addicted (in the same sense) from a single large dose of alcohol. I also know many people who have had persistent, foolish, losing bouts with alcohol — and who have had enough discomforting withdrawal symptoms to last a lifetime.

Whether in social or problem drinking, the drug action of alcohol is the same. After the effect has completely worn off, there is no physiological compulsion to repeat the experience — only memory and emotion. The social and problem drinker have only a memory of the effect achieved with liquor; the one remembers it as a pleasant interlude, the other as the only tolerable state of being. The social man returns to liquor for brain-cleansing conviviality and communication, and for brighter momentary reality. The problem man has a strong inner reluctance (in spite of his real outer desire) to leave liquor for very long for fear of trafficking with reality. One is reasonably satisfied where he is; the other has found a seemingly better place — a place where memory and self do not exist. I sometimes wonder, although I know better, what would happen if all men were created equal and practiced until they learned how to drink wisely and well. Would we then have problem drinkers as such? I doubt it. But I'm willing to wager that something else would be waiting there to worry our heads instead.

10

Liquor Around the World: Cultural Case Histories

AN important part of my work in alcoholism has required that I travel to many foreign lands. The purpose of these travels was to permit my wife and me to observe alcohol use (and the implications of its non-use), alcoholism and treatment programs in a wide variety of countries, while at the same time collecting published materials on the subjects.

We have ranged far and wide. We lived in Mexico for one year (and recently returned for another look); we have also, at one time or another, jogged our way to England, France, Switzerland, Italy, Austria, Denmark, Norway, Sweden and Finland. And at still other times, the Soviet Union, Poland, Czechoslovakia, Hungary, Yugoslavia, Rumania and Bulgaria have been among the societies we focused on. You could also add to that list the following: Greece, Turkey, Israel, Jordan, the United Arab Republic, Lebanon, Japan,

Taiwan, Hong Kong, India (including Kashmir) and Nepal. They have all tempted our appetite for firsthand knowledge about liquor and drinking attitudes.

This lovely substance, this gift of God with its innate potential for good or evil, is not only a pleasurable and satisfying liquid, it is a fascinating means (with limitless boundaries) for studying people — people of all colors, modes, beliefs and hopes, but people nevertheless.

You have seen how alcohol is fertile soil for mistaken images and frightened communication. In this part of the book I hope to provide you with some distinctive smells of some of the countries we have visited, along with their attitudes toward social drinking. And since I have mentioned poor communication, perhaps we ought to talk about the Soviet Union first.

Russia has, from my childhood, always been to me a forbidden fairyland, for it was from there that my father and mother emigrated in their youth. When in 1960 the possibility arose of a visit to the U.S.S.R. to study alcoholism, my joy abounded. Yet that moment of joy was destined for short shrift: everyone told me that alcoholism, in Russian eyes, was a problem of capitalist — not socialist — societies, and they never would admit its existence.

I contacted the East-West section of the United States State Department and was gently and kindly informed that they had been trying for some time to arrange a study exchange of professionals interested in alcoholism, but that the Soviets would not respond.

The head of an international division of the United States Public Health Service was commuting between Moscow and Washington, however, setting up cultural exchange programs, and he kindly offered to do what he could for me. He, too, reported that alcoholism was a closed subject as far as the Soviets were concerned.

Vice President (then Senator) Hubert H. Humphrey had recently returned from his eight-hour session with former Premier Nikita Krushchev and I had much contact with his office and aides. They, too, were kind but felt helpless and hopeless about effecting contacts with the Russians on alcoholism.

In desperation I located the likely looking names of some Russian psychiatrists from a government booklet on known Russian scientists and sent off some letters. The letters were an attempt to subvert (cleverly, I thought) the obvious fact with which I had been so persistently confronted: the Soviets do not admit they have any alcoholism problem. The subterfuge read as follows: "Dear Doctor, I am interested in studying the effects of alcohol on psychiatric syndromes. I am planning to visit the Soviet Union, and would like the opportunity to exchange information with my Soviet colleagues on this matter."

Within three months (and from Russia that is the equivalent of "by return mail") Professor D. D. Fedotov had responded to my plea — but in a strange way. "Dear Dr. Chafetz," he wrote, "We have not been interested in studying the effects of alcohol on psychiatric syndromes in the Soviet Union for over twenty years.

However, we are doing much work on alcoholism, and my colleagues and I would be happy to show you whatever you would like to see during your visit to our country."

The postscript really floored me. It said: "Under separate cover I am sending you a book entitled, *Alcoholism in the U.S.S.R.*" (This I subsequently received.)

I have belabored this point because of its importance: when people have to deal with societal responses they do not approve of, or are frightened of, these same people do not listen or communicate. Liquor is one such subject; the Soviet Union is another.

As it turned out, the Soviets could not have been kinder. I felt as comfortable there as I would in many parts of my own and other countries. No information I desired was completely denied me; nothing I asked for was refused, albeit there were delays and waiting. And I saw much.

The Soviets are a dynamic people. As I hinted earlier, their centuries of servitude have been scrubbed from their backs, and they proudly lift their collectivized heads to the sun. They do not know the freedom most people in the West know, of course, but then most of us have never known the kind of servitude they have experienced.

And so the Russians are justifiably proud. They are a warm, affectionate people, as I could have attested to from my infancy. Although they suffer an almost innate suspiciousness (pre-Communist in origin), they heartily devour much of what they consider to be the "good" of life. Thus, liquor *is* important to most of the Soviet people. Hard drinking has, until recently, been implicitly fostered by the "manliness" attributed to the person who could drink much and show no obvious disturbance. The heavy drinker who was abusive, disorderly or socially deviant was harshly treated as a hooligan and a criminal.

The Russians also indict hard liquor (vodka) as a culprit in possible drinking problems, but they tend to disregard the effects of wine and beer. While I was in the Soviet Union, for example, an edict was issued whereby only one glass of vodka could be served to a person in a bar or restaurant. The individual could, of course, make his way to other places where drink was sold, but drinking establishments are much fewer and farther between in the Soviet Union than in the United States. The thesis was that the drinker would metabolize his one drink before he reached the next oasis, thereby lessening the potential for intoxication. In a sense, the plan worked, since vodka consumption did subsequently fall off in the country. But here's the rub: there was at the same time a highly increased consumption of wines and beers, and an increased production of home liquors!

A further complaint voiced in the Soviet Union was that entertainment and the arts glorified, or acquiesced in, the use of liquor as a healthy part of life. The Russian people, not unlike Americans, were enticed to drink in popular songs, plays, books and movies. The leaders of the government became concerned that this attitude might interfere with production effectiveness and schedules.

Drinking among residents of collective farms is frequent and usually related to celebrations. The farm personnel are astute at finding events or people to honor by a drinking feast. In the book *Drinking and Intoxication*, Mark Field quotes V. Sapozhnikova in the *Literaturnaya Gazeta*, who described the celebration of Saint Tikhon Day as a typical example:

Visitors flooded the village of Polubabino from morning. They came from every direction to drink . . . By all accounts a notable drinking spree was in the offing. A month previous, people had begun to make home brew and to prepare refreshments. Three days before the "holiday," fifty collective farmers, more than one-fourth of the entire working force, had gone to the nearest workers' settlement to make purchases . . . glasses clinked in every house. A strong intoxicating odor of home brew pervaded the air, and discordant songs issued from the windows. . . . "Who is this Tikhon, grandmother?" I asked an old woman. "What did he do to the people to be so honored?" "Tikhon?" she replied. "Who cares? It is not for us to bother. He is home brew, that's all." . . . Those who collapsed were dragged over a fence, doused with water, and left to lie until they came to and resumed drinking. . . .

Apparently, the group practice of heavy drinking described by Sapozhnikova, although heavy in terms of amounts consumed, is not labeled "alcoholism" by the Soviets. I saw little reference to a high incidence of problem drinking among collective farmers, but more of it attributed to manual laborers in the factories and those who pursued "a life of leisure and high living."

Soviet society, as reflected by the medical profession, has much the same attitudes toward problem drinkers as American society and medicine: that is, moralistic and punitive. Medical and social disapproval of alcohol problems is manifested by frequent statements against people so afflicted, and by denying to the hospitalized alcoholic patient and his family certain benefits of the socialistic state which are normally available to patients.

Among the Soviet orbit countries, Czechoslovakia (in 1960) and Bulgaria (in 1961) responded differently. Czechslovakia is a lovely land of ancient architectural beauty. Her people bear the mark of six hundred years — save for the twenty years between the end of World War I and the Munich Pact — of servitude under the yoke of foreign invaders; their outward appearance is that of mass depression. Only with time and warmth does a spark ignite. Then smiles flash, lightness glows and liveliness appears.

The Czechs, in spite of the Communist system, have more of the feel of Western cultural desires, and I, for one, felt quite at home there. Liquor consumption is high in Czechoslovakia; as in the United States, more money is spent on alcohol than on books, movies and the theater. And, although it is a major beer-producing and beer-consuming country, hard-liquor sales continue to outstrip those of other alcoholic beverages. This socialized, industrial country does much drinking in large groups which gather together socially. While Czechoslovakia has a lower incidence of problem drinking than the United States (two per cent versus three per cent), its attitudes toward alcohol problems remain progressive and sophisticated. Czech problem drinkers have a nationwide program of treatment at many levels of endeavor and recovered patients are utilized in the care of other patients. Further, payments are provided for problem drinkers' families when the provider is hospitalized, as is the care for other medical conditions. Famous personalities who have suffered and recovered from alcoholism often come before groups of patients undergoing treatment in order to help them recover, create and maintain new self-respect. While I was there, a leading poet of the country, winner of a national prize and a onetime problem drinker, came to read his poetry before a group of such patients.

The Bulgarians, like the Czechs, are enlightened about liquor problems. Bulgaria, a small Balkan country of intense beauty, with shining seashores and verdant mountains, contains some nine million gay, warm and endearing people. I liked the Bulgars. Their ties to Russia are pre-Communist and date to 1878 when the Russians freed them from their servitude under the Turks. I saw no militant communism such as I saw in other lands (Rumania, for example), and I was treated with kindness, respect and interest wherever I ventured. Alcohol consumption is lower in Bulgaria than in other East European countries, as is the incidence of alcoholism.

In spite of this fact, it was in Bulgaria that I found myself drinking early in the morning. I had been invited to deliver a lecture before the Academy of Science on "Alcohol Problems in the United States." Great fanfare had preceded this event because, as a visiting American lecturer, I was one of the first in my field to have visited Bulgaria following the re-establishment of diplomatic relations between our two countries. Academician Uzenov, a burly but warm scientist of the old school, greeted me in his office prior to the lecture. Before us was a table laden with numerous bottles of liquor, great quantities of food, flowers for my wife and presents for me. Now, toasts at nine o'clock in the morning — especially before a lecture — are not my forte, but I gamely adjusted to my surroundings. Fortunately, there were no unpleasant aftereffects until my lecture and the formalities were over; it was then that the cultural attaché from the United States Embassy called to take us to a luncheon on our behalf. Only then, when officialdom was introduced, did the chill appear; once again I observed how communication at official levels can be strained, whereas at the man-to-man, colleague-to-colleague, scientist-to-scientist levels, such strains are minimal.

The Bulgarians, although their problems with alcohol are low in number, keep a watchful eye against any signs of a rise; and they treat those so afflicted with respect, gentleness and understanding. Only when aggressive, destructive behavior complicates matters do they become vindictive and punitive in their attitudes.

Let us leave Eastern Europe now and briefly visit the Orient. Mysterious, delicate and different, Japan beckons across the mighty Pacific. Here the opportunity for the study of drinking behavior in a culture undergoing frenzied change fascinated me. Japan and its people are many things to many people: for me, it was characterized by gentleness, consideration for others and a delight in simple beauty, with its rain-flushed forests and its temples of startling colors. Honest, industrious and helpful, the Japanese people of today are a delight to know and are far removed from the destructive creatures portrayed to us during wartime.

This extreme — between gentleness and barbarism — is not really surprising when one looks at Japan. Her people successfully combine a day-to-day, reality-oriented religion, Shintoism, with a future-oriented, symbolic religion, Buddhism. Shintoism, with its shamanistic background, contains many myths relating to sake — the alcoholic beverage of Japan that is fermented from rice. "Sake" is an abbreviation of the Japanese word for prosperity, because the merry sensations associated with drinking are thought to be equivalent to the exuberant feelings of the prosperous. The imbibing of the divine sake is intimately entwined with Shinto worship; on the other hand, the Commandments of Buddha are unrelenting in preaching total abstinence.

And yet, the Japanese have not seemed to suffer any

guilt as a consequence of this ambivalence. Prior to the end of World War II, Japan drank much and often with few alcohol problems. Drinking was a part of festivals. For example there was the New Year's Day custom, derived from the Chinese, of "toso," a mixture of medicines and sake for disease prevention. In ascending progression, the youngest first to the oldest last, they would partake of this drink to ward off the evils of sickness. At present, the toso custom in Japan is nothing more than drinking sake to celebrate the New Year.

The Doll's Festival (Shirozake), on March 3, is celebrated by the preparation of a white sake. Dolls of prominent Japanese, from the Emperor down, and fruits of orange and cherry are integral parts of this drinking and eating festival, during which all members of the family and their guests share cups of the wine. Moon-viewing and moonlight parties are other occasions for sake partaking. Under sparkling, clear autumn skies, the romantic and poetic drink their mighty measure of sake, devour their dumplings of boiled flour and compose poems to the full moon bathing them in its light.

The Shinto wedding, like that of the Jews, unites the couple not only with prayer but by a sharing of the sacred cup of wine. Sake is offered to the couple in three different cups at three different times; in addition, harvest time, cherry-blossom time, and other moments of nature and history are celebrated by much drink. But the Japanese, as noted, never had to concern themselves with alcohol problems — until the end of the war changed their whole outlook. Attitudes and values formerly cherished have been rapidly discarded and replaced by unfamiliar American ones. The mingling and mixing of things Oriental and Occidental is common in today's Japan: bars, cafes, nightclubs, cabarets and all manner of places serving liquor abound in the big cities. The neon signs flood you with their nightly brightness, the blaring noise of popular song penetrates the sound of moving hordes of people in the streets, and everywhere the enticements to come in and drink and dance with the ubiquitous hostesses are flaunted. In Japan, a man cannot drink without a hostess to keep him company; indeed, the need for so many girls to become hostesses has led to the saying: "It takes years to become a Geisha; it takes but one night to become a hostess."

Weekend intoxication is more common in the Japan of today because the Japanese people have more leisure available to them. Young people are less involved in religious activities and women now have more to occupy them outside their homes. Concomitant with these cultural changes has been a rising rate of alcohol problems. The Japanese, as before, tend to be lenient toward the intoxicated, so long as he is not violent. While I was there (in 1963), a judge sentenced two men to prison for two years because they had "caused death by abandoning a person in a state of temporary illness due to advanced intoxication." The enlightened Japanese court ruled that the person who becomes ill from liquor is the responsibility of his friends. They are to care for him until he regains self-control, because in the eyes of the court, a drunk man is a sick man. Abandoning him, therefore, is criminal. The two imprisoned gentlemen had left their intoxicated companion in a railroad yard and he was unable to avoid the railroad train that later ran him down.

To the south of Japan, nestled on the island of Taiwan, lies all that is left of Free China. My real desire was to study Chinese drinking patterns on the mainland, but political realities prevented this. Rising abruptly from the China Sea, Taiwan is like a lazy island that wishes merely to be left alone. But this is destined not to be, for Taiwan has been overrun since the late forties by hordes of Chinese who fled the Communist takeover on the mainland. The island has great natural beauty, with lush forests and vibrant, exotic-looking blossoms, and yet, while the landscape is vibrant, the people are less so. This is not surprising; packed into a tight little island with no place to go, the people and the aging government sustain themselves with one of the grossest fantasies of all time: the invasion and conquering of the Red tyrants on the mainland but a moment away. Encased in their unreality, little of permanence is provided to the Taiwanese; their roots seek only surface sustenance.

In spite of obvious discomfort and suffering, buffered by the frequent use of liquor, the Taiwanese are essentially without alcohol problems. The Chinese seem to have that cultural something that permits them to adopt the same sensible drinking attitudes common to the Orthodox Jew and the native Italian. In China, too, liquor drinking can be traced far back to ancient ceremonials, such as weddings, burials and libations to the gods, all of which were commonly drenched with beverage alcohol. This mixture of a cultural attitude of Confucian placidity with the invention of liquor primarily to drown sorrows has been a successful marriage through eons of Chinese history.

A closer look at the Chinese method of drinking gives us a clue why they enjoy the beneficial effects of liquor without suffering its devastating complications. For one thing, the Chinese almost never drink alone — drinking occurs only at parties and at mealtime. Liquor is used for — and is expected to promote — communication between people. Furthermore, social disapproval of drunkards is strong and clear-cut; one must behave with friends and strangers at all times in well-defined ways. The Chinese themselves stress that they are different from other people in the way they drink. They sip while others gulp; they prefer to be seated while drinking and it is rare to see a Chinese standing at a bar rapidly downing his liquor. Although the Chinese may drink slowly, it does not necessarily follow that they drink less. It's just that they prefer to get where they are going pleasurably, rather than painfully. (I do not mean to imply that the Chinese do not take in

healthy amounts at single swallows. This is not so. Some
Chinese toasts are often downed a full cup at a time —
three in all, one after the other!)

While the Chinese have many excuses for imbibing,
they would never consider drinking without eating.
Food and drink are, to them, healthfully entwined. To
emphasize the place of honor for liquor among many
Chinese — after the dishes have been placed and the
rice bowls filled — only the head of the household may
drink while the other family members eat. "First to
start and last to finish" is the drinking honor imparted
to heads of Chinese households.

To the Chinese way of thinking, drinkers from other
cultures are uncivilized in their drinking behavior.
Foreigners can never appreciate the full value of
liquor, according to the Chinese, because they insist on
pouring large amounts rapidly down their gullets as
though they were quenching thirst, instead of savoring
and appreciating each drop as though it came from
God, which is the Chinese custom.

Thailand, the ancient kingdom of Siam, is another
country of incomparable beauty whose drinking
behavior is worth study. Lush tropical vegetation, inter-
laced with graceful canals, marks its capital city, Bang-
kok, and provides a setting of unmatched loveliness. Not
alone in the magnificence of its earth, Thailand contains brilliant temples of flashing multicolored shapes
and styles. Furthermore, the Thai people themselves
are a joy to the eye. I have yet to behold another race

of people of such uniform beauty and elegance. Moreover, their beauty of face and figure is complemented by a beauty of personality: they laugh easily, they emote unashamedly, they love deeply, and they take much pleasure in the gift of life.

Social drinking is common to Thailand, and liquor consumption is high (there are few regulations affecting liquor consumption at all). The poorer classes drink strong "jungle whiskey" distilled from fermented rice, and also a less potent beverage derived from coconut-palm juices, mixed with yeast powder and fermented for five to seven days. These native liquors contain many impurities, which do not appear to be harmful to the Thais.

For generations the Thais were a people famous for their close, strong family ties, and most pleasures were taken within the confines of the family. Prior to the imposition of Occidental cultural values following World War II, male and female roles were clearly delineated and the matter of what was correct behavior for men or for women was simply not a problem. This is no longer so. Family closeness has broken down, women now have occupations outside the home for economic reasons, and the tendency to seek pleasure outside the home has become more common. Interestingly enough, Thai problem drinkers appear to fall into the class of occupations which carry them *away* from family and home influence: policemen, chauffeurs, actors, bus drivers, locomotive operators and sailors, for example.

While Thai drinking today is heavy in amount, it is

combined with heavy eating. The visitor, whether guest in a humble hut or an opulent palace, is greeted with a continuous proffering of food and drink. Drinking in Thailand is rarely of the solitary kind and is almost always carried on in the presence of much food and many people — a combination which points unmistakably in the direction of healthy drinking experiences.

In my circling of the globe, I shall skip over the subcontinent of India and set down on the tiny country of Lebanon. A beige dot of land on one edge of the brazenly blue Mediterranean, Lebanon conjoins Western and Middle Eastern values. With its great natural beauty — the rich, abundant fields, the pleasant mountain peaks that seemingly spring from the shore, the archeological finds to delight the imaginative — and a kind, overly generous people, this small nation has much to recommend it.

Because the Lebanese have learned the cost of political instability, they go to great ends to accommodate both Arab and European, Moslem and Christian. They are heavy eaters and heavy drinkers. Arak, the popular licorice-tasting alcoholic drink there, is manufactured in a romantic little place named Zahle. Clear arak, like absinthe and anisette, takes on a cloudy hue when mixed with water; it is consumed with a wide variety of different foods on Arab bread. So if you are dieting, don't go to Lebanon. In social situations, food is offered to establish an interpersonal relationship. It is not only offered, it is fed to you. To refuse is insulting.

Also, be careful not to misinterpret the seemingly seductive feeding of a man by a beauteous young woman as a hint of something more. The Lebanese, in their uninhibited joy of living and giving, behave this way to make sure that you know that they are ecstatically happy that you are in their land. This hours-long activity of eating (and being fed) huge amounts of food and drink by men and women is difficult — if not impossible — to stop until all drink and food have been consumed.

Since there is so much eating and communicating going on while you drink, it is perhaps not strange that aftereffects are almost nonexistent. Solitary drinking is unthinkable in Lebanon (anything solitary is unthinkable here), and the incidence of alcoholism is extremely low.

Very similar to the Lebanese in face, figure and uninhibited emotion is the Italian. The variety of possible pleasures for the eye, ear, nose and mouth available to the lover of life in Italy has been described since ancient times. The Italians are as warm and as freely expressive as any people can be on the earth, and I love them. They make me feel at home. Their feelings are real, and they don't act as though they were playing a role. The Italian man and woman — especially the latter — have more confidence and self-respect in Italy than those Italians who are natives of other lands. To my taste and eye, the women are more beautiful, the men more handsome than Italians in my own land. This, of course, may be a product of the romantic bias that colors the eye of the loving traveler.

What pleased me — besides the art, the land, the people and a host of other pleasures — was the Italian way of drinking. In a few words, the native Italian drinks as he does most everything: naturally. He makes no fuss about it. When the Italian sits in a restaurant with his wife and children and friends, the wine is just another substance on the table. The children are provided their fair share, and I believe that everyone knows — or ought to — that Italy has little or no problems with alcohol. Drinking becomes a way of life early; it is then that liquor becomes a staple of diet for always. Thus, the problems that Italians develop later do not manifest themselves in alcoholism. (There is evidence, however, that when Italians move to another culture and take on the drinking attitude of, say, the Americans, they begin to develop alcohol problems. In other words, the protection available to the native Italian, where his drinking is concerned, becomes lost when he finds himself in a culture where unhealthy attitudes toward liquor exist.)

I have often believed that we could learn a great deal from the natural attitude of the Italian toward liquor, but I suspect that our chauvinism prevents this; we find it difficult, in general, to believe that we can learn from other nations.

The two European countries whose drinking behavior is often compared are Italy and France. Although I love France, I feel closer to the Italians than to the French; I feel that the latter are not as free and natural. They *play* at life roles. It is as though the French people believe that they are expected to behave a certain way and they expend all their energy fulfilling this image. This is true, in my opinion, in almost everything they do: sex, dress, personal relationships, drinking and so forth. Their expression of feeling is more inhibited than the Italian; they are less deeply committed, and drinking is for functional purposes mainly. Let me elaborate.

All sections of France produce some kind of brandy. This comes from the fact that the farmers of France, who are permitted to make liquor for their own use, produce an extra amount for sale. This leads to an attitude of benevolence toward illegal traffic in liquor, and underlines the difficulties in ever procuring accurate figures on liquor consumption in the country. Furthermore, the Frenchman believes that whether he drinks wine, brandy or other alcohol beverages, it is all good for him. The attitude of most French workers is that it is impossible for him to work *without* alcohol in some form or other. This is what I mean when I refer to the unhealthy use of drink for functional purposes: you cannot meet a friend in France without being offered alcohol, and you would never think of having a workman in your house do an odd job without offering him something to drink. At all social stations in France, alcohol is there to celebrate success, drown a sorrow, or to produce the proper mental attitude for work.

Thus, liquor in France has special, magical qualities ascribed to it. Beside being wholesome and strength-giving, it is believed to produce pleasant traits of character — it makes one happy, carefree or humorous. Bravery can be ascribed to the use of a special brand of liquor, as well as medical cure; in other words, the French are given the impression through their history, literature and social attitudes that they could not survive or function in life without alcohol. It has become, seemingly, a necessity of life, which only encourages them to drink still more. Nondrinkers can cast a heavy pall indeed on any social situation if they so choose.

With this attitude toward liquor, the French have created more alcohol problems for themselves than most other nations. One healthy French attitude I learned about recently, however, concerned a practice now existing in French mental hospitals. Here a portion of liquor is served to the patient as part of his fare to help him relax and communicate with other patients. We ought to try this, as I have suggested earlier, in our own hospitals with patients who must remain over prolonged periods.

With all my skipping around the world, I always enjoy returning home to my own country with a fresh outlook on our drinking attitudes. But, few countries I have observed are threatened today by the one aspect of American drinking behavior which I find especially impressive and worrisome: *when many Americans drink, they behave as though they are sinning.* Therefore, drinking together is like sinning together, and this results in much guilt.

And so, if I have made any points in this book, I hope this is the one that sinks in deepest and longest: it's about time Americans stopped wasting so much of their lives worrying about sin. I trust, where liquor is concerned, I have made myself abundantly clear on that point.

Epilogue

I<small>F</small> I said to you simply, "I drink," you might well think to yourself: "What a shame. Such a nice man. How his family must suffer!"

The truth of the matter is that not only do I drink but so do my wife and children. I love life and I love pleasure. I'm not talking about the pleasures of the body alone but all pleasures. I like the feeling that the bite of cold, clear air makes in my lungs as I stand alone with my skis on top of a mountain. I find pleasure in letting my eyes wander over an ancient or foreign city, in watching the clouds pass by in the sky, in observing the symphony of leaves as they turn in the fall. I thrill to the sound of music, to the sound of children laughing with life, to all the noises that tell me life goes on.

There are those who are afraid of life and pleasure. When they do permit themselves to drink, for example, it is often done unwisely, perhaps to quell the torture of a deep sense of inadequacy. In time, the liquor softens the pain of their emotional isolation and they begin to reach out for anyone in their environment. Consideration and politeness leave, intimacies are revealed; you listen to much you'd rather not hear — his boring tales, his bad luck, his real thoughts about you, his marital problems, his ungrateful children, and so on.

Readers of this book, of course, do not use liquor in this manner; you know the true value of drink. You, too, like to take pleasure from the gift of life, and no words I can offer will recall sufficiently the pleasure, sight, taste and smell of wine. Some wines will pass quickly from the palate's memory like a passing acquaintance, while others linger forever like a true friend. (No doubt you know the liquor snob who bandies brands and vintages and compares good drink to women, sex, fast cars, old architecture, and so forth. Thurber parodied it beautifully and ultimately with his caption under a drawing of two wine snobs: "This is rather a presumptuous little wine. I hope you will pardon its impertinence.")

Now that we have reached this point in our positive perusal of liquor, what do we have? No one questions the statement that liquor is popular throughout much of the world, and that this is unusually true in the United States. Whether all, or some, or none of our suggested explanations for these phenomena seem reasonable, there the world is and there the world seems content to remain. Apart from any of the evidence and arguments — both historical and technical — no one who has confidence in people seems to think it likely that they will get stirred up anew over prohibition. As soon as people decide there is too much drinking, statistics on alcohol consumption will show a decline. To date, the majority must not have so decided, for we are consuming about one hundred seventy million gallons of whiskey in the United States a year.

The same proof is not available for individuals, but we do have many rough measuring rods which enable a person to gauge his drinking. Do you drink more than others in your group? Are you the one always pressing for the next round? Do you lie about how much you have had? Are your work and family life being crowded out of first place? Do you lose interest in food when drinking? If so, you're in trouble.

Most drinkers do not have trouble. Normal social drinkers are those to whom a good night's sleep represents the end of a drinking occasion; to the problem drinker, however, it means an unusually long period of abstinence. The point of the proof is that liquor, for the problem drinker, has become essential even to temporary peace of mind. Within social drinking practices, the lack of definition is of no great matter. Most people enjoy figuring out our drinking habits; interestingly, the figuring usually concerns individual occasions rather than liquor as a constant factor, and the variability of personal opinion as to what constitutes too much drinking is as wide as the variability among the people themselves.

There is indeed amusement in the extremes. Nearly all of us have met the man who thinks he is a hellion once a year on New Year's Eve after a glass of elderberry wine. At the next level, there is the one who thinks he'd better watch it because hardly a week has gone by for months when he did not at some time or other take a drink. Meanwhile, at the opposite pole, there peals forth this old ditty:

> *He is not drunk who from the floor*
> *Can rise again, and drink once more,*
> *But he is drunk, who prostrate lies,*
> *And cannot drink and cannot rise.*

Even this leniency has been viewed as too harsh, as witness the following dialogue regarding the bylaws of the "Sublime Society of the Free and Easy Club":

MR. BOWKER: It is enacted that no member shall be considered drunk or liable to the pains and penalties contingent upon intoxication if he can lie without holding.

MR. MOONFACE: Then after he is incapacitated from walking, if he can lie still on the floor, is he considered sober?

MR. BOWKER: He is not considered drunk.

They come more tolerant than that, too. In 1532, Arnaud de Villeneuve advised: "Whoever wakes up with a hangover ought to ask himself the reason for his drunkenness. If it be lack of habitude he ought to recommence his drinking to habituate himself to wine and avoid drunkenness."

So how much is too much is any man's guess. If you are anywhere near the center and between the extremes, you probably give the matter very little thought; but any facts on the subject must obviously involve consideration of individual tolerance, personality and body weight. At the same alcoholic blood level one person may, to outward appearances, be unaffected and another sloppily tight. One may be quiet and morose and the other entirely too much the life of the party. One may be pale and nauseated and the other unable to vomit in spite of stringent emetic measures.

What then can we say about our liquor education? We can say with some assurance:

That alcohol is a poison and will kill you quickly and surely, but no more quickly and no more surely than distilled water, if you drink too much of it at one time. That alcohol is actually manufactured in the human body but is less poisonous than most of the other natural secretions such as thyroid, pituitary, adrenal, pancreas and bile. That alcohol, if taken in anything remotely approaching customary amounts, is harmless to the body and in many cases beneficial.

That alcohol is one of the most valuable medicines in the world both as a sedative and as a food, is useful for these and other reasons in many disease conditions, and can be most important in old age and in chronic illness.

That alcohol and fornication do not go well together since they offset each other in ego blandishment; and furthermore, that alcohol in heavy amounts plays the low trick of encouraging sex to rear its head — and then knocking it off.

That alcohol has had a conspicuous position in the history of the race. It had some parentage in religion and science and agriculture, provided more human confidence, and promoted good will toward men. It is an efficient and practical relaxer of the driving force in the brain; it offers an immediate method of personal enjoyment; it is a great medium for the purpose of permitting man to forget, at least for a little while, the shortness of life and the ludicrously helpless and infinitesimal part he plays in the functions of the universe.

That alcohol as an intoxicant has its toxicity increased and not decreased by aging, or by the congeners or substances mixed with it to make it more palatable. Properly distilled neutral spirits contain a minimum of these congeners, such as volatile and nonvolatile acids, aldehydes, furfural, tannins, esters, terpenes, glycerine, sugar, albumin, and so on, and it is at the door of these that can be placed many of the drinking distresses such as nausea, diarrhea, and gastro-intestinal irritation. Most of the famous drinks have a long history and are hard to improve, but their most healthful form is a simple form.

That alcohol used regularly, a bit every day, is not the danger. The danger lies in overindulgence and intoxication whereby one increases the possibility of foolish and dangerous behavior.

That alcohol usage has always fallen into line to fit the conventions of a given people at a given time. It is so today. The average drinker equalizes restraint with release by indulgence within his personal capacity and situation. Undue restraint is as unhealthy and stifling as excess in the other direction. Emotional miserliness, persistent and insistent denial of feelings, can be the root of mental disturbance more often than overindulgence. Many an individual suffering with depression, despondency, brooding, paralysis of decision, obsessive ruminations, or any other neurotic manifestations can trace his problem to long-standing thwarting of his natural feelings. On the other side of the coin, a gluttonous lack of restraint is similarly destructive to mind and body; if we find ourselves habitually overdrinking certainly we cannot blame the liquor for what is wrong inside ourselves.

And finally, we can say that alcohol has existed longer than all human memory. It has outlived generations, nations, epochs and ages. It is a part of us, and that is fortunate indeed. For although alcohol will always be the master of some, for most of us it will continue to be the servant of man.

Selected Reading List

In my preparation for this book, certain authors especially influenced my thinking.

Drinking and Intoxication. Edited by Raymond G. McCarthy. Glencoe, Illinois: The Free Press, 1959.

This book contains a wealth of information on a wide variety of subjects but was especially helpful to me in providing historical material and confirming some observations I made on my own in various foreign lands.

The Complete Imbiber. Edited by Cyril Ray. New York: Rhinehart and Company, Inc., 1957.

This entertaining volume is made up of a number of delightful stories extolling the virtue of drink and provided me with some of the flavor I sought for this book.

Primitive Drinking. A study of the uses and functions of alcohol in preliterate societies. Chandler Washburne. New York: College and University Press, 1961.

In Praise of Wine and Certain Noble Spirits. Alec Waugh. New York: William Sloane Associates, 1959.

The book provided me with some historical material and was a delight to read for general background and tone.
Society, Culture, and Drinking Patterns. Edited by David J. Pittman and Charles R. Snyder. New York: John Wiley and Sons, Inc., 1962.

Should Christians Drink? An objective inquiry. Everett Tilson. New York: Abingdon Press, 1957.
This little book contains many useful biblical references.

Treasury of Wine and Wine Cookery. Greyton H. Taylor. New York: Harper and Row, 1963.
Contains some interesting historical data.

The Neutral Spirit: A Portrait of Alcohol. Berton Roueche. Boston: Little, Brown and Company, 1960.
A masterful examination of alcohol which provided me with much background material of a historical nature. It was useful also in my preparation of Chapters 2 and 3. I recommend this book highly.

Alcoholism and Society. Morris E. Chafetz and Harold W. Demone, Jr. New York: Oxford University Press, 1962.

Alcohol and Traffic Safety. Edited by Bernard H. Fox and James H. Fox. Washington, D.C.: United States Government Printing Office, 1963.
This book reports on a symposium held at a national conference in Pittsburgh (1961) on alcohol and traffic safety. The article by Ira H. Cisin furnished me with some valuable background material for Chapter 7.

Alcohol and Civilization. Edited by Salvatore P. Lucia. New York: McGraw-Hill Book Company, Inc., 1963.

A History of Wine as Therapy. Salvatore P. Lucia. Philadelphia: J. B. Lippincott Company, 1963.
These two volumes were a valuable source of material for me in Chapters 1, 2 and 3. They are valuable additions to the alcohol literature and I recommend them highly.

Encyclopaedia Britannica. 1954 Edition. Sections on Wine and Fermentation. Chicago: Encyclopaedia Britannica, Inc.

In addition, my colleague, Howard Blane, has kindly furnished me with some of the material he plans to use in a forthcoming paper on liquor and crime; it forms the nucleus for Chapter 6.

And finally, columnist Russell Baker of the *New York Times* has, with great wit, focused on some of our social responses and problems of the day; his approach has been of great benefit to me.

Index